Spiritual Seduction

BY PAX

Moose Ear Press
P.O. Box 2422
Clarkesville, Georgia 30523
800.899.2464

FIRST HARDCOVER EDITION 2002

For more information on seminars, books and tapes by
Jerry Stocking, please see the back pages of this book.

Editor: Tracey Johnson
Copy Editor: Karen Blum and Karen M. Bates
Contributing Editor: Dr. Fred Blum
Cover Design: Zoë Snyder
Universal Power Supply: Karen M. Bates

CONTRIBUTIONS:
Lorraine Hamilton
Wayne Furnweger

ISBN 0-9629593-8-3

DEDICATION

This book is dedicated to the bravery in each of us.

TABLE OF CONTENTS

FOREWORD TO SEDUCTION

Gentle Reader, I am hoping that you are the kind of person who, when confronted with a very curvy, maybe mountainous road, slows down, pays close attention and very aggressively learns the road in hopes that you will get a chance to travel it at high speed, almost risking life and limb and having the drive of a lifetime. If you are that kind of person or hope to be this book is for you. If you don't like the curvy road, if you prefer the straight and narrow, the freeway, the toll way or some other similar uninspiring root to somewhere, something or somebody else, this book may be a worthwhile challenge.

There she is, my new editor, about eight-minutes-old. She is sitting confidently at the computer but with a look I will remember and hope to see on you. She looks something like she has just had sex and gas too. I have never seen her right after sex, but I wouldn't be able to write this book if I ruled that out. I have never seen her with gas either, but there is a universality to both looks that when combined is undeniable. A few minutes later she comes into my kitchen and says, "Are the run-on sentences intentional?" I say, in the nicest way I know how, "I did those so that people would extend what they consider to be a complete thought. As Einstein taught us, if something goes fast enough for long enough it gets younger, I figured that if fast enough for long enough could do that we should maybe find out what long enough for long enough would do which is why you will find at least forty percent less periods in my play than in my work. Yes, they are intentional, they go on to show you just how long life can be when you don't understand where you are going. They are, and I invite you to treat them nicely, your key to immortality." She looked at me.

I, of course, went on, "You may be tempted upon starting this book to think thoughts like, 'I want this to be the last book I ever read. This has all the answers, he really knows what he is talking about (which makes one of him).'" Remember, and this is important, that this is only the beginning of our relationship, the stage in which you either have a crush on me or want me to go away, and it is hard to tell which because sometimes, in these things, your stomach and your mind disagree.

Later on you may well think thoughts like, "I wish he would die." "This is the dumbest thing I ever read." "I don't think that I ever will read another book." "If I had a hammer I'd hammer in the morning." "Why do I understand this, and why do I like myself and my life better when reading it?" "If I had a gun and two bullets I don't even remember whether I would shoot him first or myself and then finish him off." "I really am this smart, isn't life grand?" This book is intended to take the order of things and

interrupt it.

As a beginner at the particular kind of discomfort able pleasure I secrete I invite you to add your own punctuation to the book if you want to. While there is such a thing as copyright law this does not apply to what you do to one copy of my book. I do though humbly, that's a joke, request that when we meet, and we will, that you don't show me your changes, of the book that is, but that you let me know just how many punctuation marks of different types, the sum if you will, you were able to inject while still maintaining the susceptibility to the practical upswing and rise in intelligence certainly available in this book.

An exhibitionist is someone who shows parts of himself in public he shouldn't: this varies by culture. A turbo exhibitionist is one who writes a revealing book. We need more female exhibitionists; we need more female philosophers too. Teasing is pretending to be an exhibitionist when you are not one. At one level this can mean showing only so much, at another level it means not being truly present while showing more. To make Earth more livable we need fewer habitionists period. You can have your Cro Magnon period, your Neanderthal period, your Age of Reason, all in one lifetime, but please give me, on the way to the Omnipotent period, an Exhibitionist period. In the Exhibitionist period Easter is banned and people can just come and go as they please, dying and being reborn without all the fuss.[1] People could reveal everything about themselves and then come back to Earth to dig for more. I am ready for that period now. Read this book and we will be there together. Just you and me looking into each other's "I's" lovingly. I do love you.

Have you ever wanted a break? This book is it. It is a break from pretending. It is a break from lying. It is a break from being some degree of stupid you may call smart. It is a break from wasting your time on useless distinctions. It is a break from having to fake it and settle for less. It is a break from the absence of humor that wandering through the root, canal or tunnel you call life stores in your shoulders for all to see. This book is a break for me. It has been easy and impossible to write. It should, thus, be easy and impossible to read. I forgive you in advance for the opinions about me this book may inspire. Know please, that when you get mad, happy, sad or just plain livid that the book didn't inspire anything that wasn't in you already and that in this inspiration, readily available, on every page, will come a more creative, loving, and unpredictable you. It will move you from being the roots of the evolutionary tree to being the fruit. Read on and you will get wiser, happier, deeper, more human and more like God. What haven't you got to lose?

---

[1] When I was younger I used to think that I wanted to be able to be invisible, now that I am much older I would like to be able to have rest time not count toward how long I live. Rest time being defined as time without any pressure on. While pressure turns coal to diamonds it tends to turn people to righteous mush, no thank you.

If you don't lose a kingdom and gain a kingdom in the length of times it takes an ordinary someone to explain one of their problems then you need this book.[2]

For those bibliophiles among you who buy books but don't read them[3] I suggest that you consider the words of a close friend of mine who has earned my friendship all eight billion times he has tested it: "By any definition, if those thousands of books I have read were books this is not, this is something else entirely."

---

[2] Willingness to be edited is a characteristic of someone not mature enough as a writer to be published in a culture that prizes literature, where is that culture? Being published as such produces a well-known person too immature for fame, thus a role model doing time, and running out of time but due, always, for an untimely fall from the spotlight and grace. I am falling already but I am not falling out I am filling in. I invite you to fall too. Fall into this book. This is a book that you can tell both friend and enemy about because it will have positive repercussions, regarding you, for both.

[3] If my plan worked, by the time you are holding this book in your hands you have paid enough American dollars for it to inspire you to get the most out of it you can.

HOUSE OF CORRECTIONS

This is a get-out-of-grammatical-jail-free book. I am surprised at how many people think someday they will write a book and how few people do it. I imagine that part of the reason for this imbalance is the writing process itself. If you try and write right your creativity may be beaten off by form. Even if you try and right write you are still trying to please something other than the most creative wild parts of yourself. How about you just write and find out what happens.[1]

This is my sixth book. Four of the six have had real editors and real proof writers, this one and *Enlightenment is Losing Your Mind* didn't. I couldn't find an editor who could figure out what was being said. They all slaughtered the intent, benefit, and lightness while maybe having the text flow. They missed the point.

There are no mistakes in this manuscript. There are new conventions, odd uses, intentional permutations, invitations to react or think a word should be hyphenated, spelled differently or deleted.

Our dad is hanging out on high: just isn't the same as: Our Father who art in Heaven: or: Our Father whose art's in Heaven. Each phrase inspires something different, with the first being kind of relaxed and maybe even drug related, the second brings back religious training or reaction to same, while the third has to tickle your funny bone. Each sentence in this book is the way it was delivered to me. It is the best it can be without me in the way.

Are there run-on sentences where it is even hard to figure out what the subject is, you bet there are, and these are intended to threaten and then vastly expand what you consider to be a complete thought stretching your attention span and your

---

[1] Let's let your third, fourth and fifth grade teachers who tried to teach you grammar rest in peas. Not that diaphragming sentences can't be fun. Shhhhhhh, it can bee.

appreciation for artistic and not so artistic connections in the process. Many of the double meanings will even save you money. Finding them will make you more intelligent, they will save dollars on your doctor bills by having you be humored and thus healthier and happier,[2] they will save you donuts because instead of buying many books you can read this one over and over observing the changes all over your life: sliding where you used to crawl, flying where you used to walk and laughing where you used to stern.

There are plaze on words lurking nearly everywhere. Please celebrate when you find them, please celebrate when you don't. You will always either find them or not, so, should you take my advice, you will always be celebrating. Surprise yourself by finding your reactions and enjoying them. Sporadically unconventional and trusting are always closer to spirituality than any consistency or rule followed.

This is your book, thanks for letting me write it, and thanks for not trying to right it yourself.

---

[2] You may think I am grasping here, I am always grasping. I invite you to grasp too, always, then let go.

CHAPTER 1

Swimming Downhill

Y ou may think that I am a silly heart and you would be
right. You might think that you are not a silly heart and
you would be wrong.

There are many different forms of human to hopefully human
interaction. The worst of these is the shallow banter that results
from superficial interaction, smoothing the surface while ignoring
nearly everything else. The best of which is the dance between
deep teacher and student where the student is completely open,
surrendering and the teacher is so wise as to be open, available,
learning and connected to the universe. All the spaces in
between these extremes are filled with degrees of seduction.

Seduction is the conversion of no all the way to yes under
the scrutiny of attention. Attention is the focus of consciousness. Thus consciousness is present at the birth of yes from no.
We have had thousands of people do courses over the years. On
the entrance form to most of these courses we ask people,
among other interesting things, what the best experience of
their life was, defined as the moment that moved them most
deeply. Well over ninety percent of the people report that being
in attendance at the birth process was their most moving
moment. Both men and women answer the question with the
same experience. The birth process is our most graphic metaphor
for seduction. It is both the movement from no to yes and the
journey from inside to outside. It is the transition from dependent

to independent. The birth process is the ultimate seduction, though it is seldom perceived that way or often, it seems, experienced that way.

DROWNING, ALMOST

For the birth process to go easily consciousness needs to observe without interfering. It needs to give up a model based in control and relax into the naturalness of the event. This same strategy works in every aspect of life, not as a pat answer but as a discovery.

I have recently taken up swimming, at the tender age of fifty. Crawling in utero. Swimming has always been something I did, way in over my head, with a controlled panic, longing and waiting for land (add in expecting to die each moment and you about got the picture). I was born without gill or guile, now against the current I am swimming a mile. I have never been to Venice nor wanted to go: my life was about as un-Venice-like as it could be, until I began to swim. I started by flinging my arms and legs around, looking at the other side of the pool longingly and wondering why so many of the lifeguards seemed to be the girl, medium height, blond, pretty, uncaring and aloof, that I had never given a chance to reject me in high school but who had remained analogous to what I wanted in a woman. "If I could just have me one of those then my life would be complete." Well, the one thing I didn't want to do in front of one of those was look as silly as I did each time I went swimming. It was little consolation that these little goddesses probably weren't watching me anyway. If they were watching, it was more likely out of wondering if I needed CPR than wanting desperately to kiss me.

Anti Las Vegas, I kept going to the pool. I would swim a quarter of a mile in about an hour with any odd mixture of side stroke, breast stroke and backstroke. I would watch the barrel chested swimmers doing the crawl and passing me mercilessly. I looked for their gills, I had fun; I was watching the chicks and getting my exercise too. I was so busy telling myself that I was having fun that I really couldn't work on my lack of strokes.

The old dog drowned. I learned new tricks. Moving a body through water is a very interesting thing. There is such subtle and persistent resistance that it seems to inspire an even greater resistance. A babe with flailing arms, I began to crawl. One lap at a time, out of breath, giddy and nearly senseless I worked my way up in about three months to one half, then three quarters, then a mile. My breath came, as though I was meant to be doing this. A Bonus: I moved differently while on land, more agile, happier, thinking more clearly, and my body re-shaped. In short, I became a swimmer. I began to apply my skills as a thinker to swimming, exploring what made sense and what didn't. It didn't hurt that my best friend in the world swims nearly forever effortlessly and has taught herself to do so from scratch, it may have helped that I have tried maybe eight times in my life to climb this same water wall, to crawl effectively and efficiently knowing that I would but couldn't, it didn't help at all that anytime my father tried to swim he went backwards. He gave up.[1]

I got swimming by degrees and in the process learned much about life. There were big breakthroughs and small breakthroughs. There were set backs that looked like they were going to deter me and little ones that just filled my head for a lap or two. Swimming contains about as few variables as possible. While one is learning something new and foreign variables are neither welcome nor useful. I am tempted to jump to the

---

[1] He didn't really formerly give up swimming, I don't think he thought it was worth such a formal denial. I have so many memories of him, when he was a child, his father a milkman and him eating butter on the rounds, and these join the ones of him, after years playing oboe in the Chicago Symphony Orchestra, trying to play guitar. "Fingers aren't supposed to do this," he said as he jumped from the guitar player's plane.

biggest, recent breakthrough first thus think I will, since temptation seems currently to be sufficient motivation for almost anything.[2]

Three days ago I learned how to swim, how to do the crawl effortlessly for a mile or more. Gestation of this very welcome baby was seven and a half months into my swimming career. I have not yet dated a lifeguard but have been in many pools and done many miles. I may rather swim than have sex but can't really figure out why I can't have both, so do. Three days ago I discovered that in doing the crawl the legs do almost all the work while the arms only push for a very tiny bit in the mid-section, as they pass by the front of the body. For the first time, three days ago, I relaxed, I let the water tell me what to do and it told me perfectly. I expended no effort and went from twenty-one strokes for 25 meters to sixteen strokes for the same distance. I flowed, I gave up the fight, I left the slave ship for the nearly dolphin express. I gave in and wondered if it even counted as swimming since it was so easy. Almost immediately I wondered if all of life could be this way. I imagined how many times I had resisted things and what life would be like if it weren't just degrees of resistance. If the crawl, which I had always considered impossible but desirable was infinitely easy

---

[2] I have discovered that temptation tends to present itself several times but seldom does it get sweeter smelling with repetition. The solution to this, perhaps not clearly a dilemma, is that I, whenever possible, which has been every time so far, almost, take it the first time so it doesn't have to wear itself out in the mere process of offering. This works quite well and by such speedy integration of temptation I have discovered that unlike problems temptations often don't have other temptations right underneath them. Sometimes I have to wait, sometimes for minutes but never for seconds or thirds, before a new temptation shows up to guide me the way I really ought to be going in my life. Studies show that the average person spends 1.43435243 seconds without a problem throughout a lifetime. Temptations by their unstacked nature, have that lag then bolt time in between that always makes them a welcome visitor and sometimes a bedfellow.

and effortless, why couldn't other aspects of life be? If the impossible is easy then maybe everything else could be too. Duhhhhhhhh.

Though this seems obvious, if you have seen one miracle you have not seen them all, applying this to all aspects of life is something to be—something to hold, something to behold, then let go of. Maybe, just maybe things are supposed to be easy, simple, trouble free, uncomplicated and smooth. Maybe just maybe we are to glide effortlessly through life learning exactly what we need each step to make the most of the next step. Maybe being seduced by life is as easy as letting go and as hard as letting go. Maybe we are life not some alien being trying to fit ourselves into it. Maybe seduction is the key to life. Maybe we need to either always be seducing or seduced. Maybe there is no difference between the two. Maybe each two is one and we don't really have to make it so: complicated.

CHAPTER 2

Traveling Light

I have known for many years that we are all enlightened but that few of us know it. I have known that we have already arrived and that we just need to notice our arrival to be sufficiently full of appreciation to flow effortlessly through every aspect of life. I have discovered, which is better than knowing, that you can't live just on desserts but you can live perfectly on just desserts: karma with a chari on it. Knowing this isn't experiencing it and experiencing it isn't knowing it and knowing and experiencing it doesn't necessarily mean that one can impart it to another and knowing it and experiencing it and being able to impart it to another doesn't necessarily mean another will be able to maintain it on his or her own. "Has your baggage been under your own control and did you accept anything from any suspicious looking people?" Well, sort of no then yes.[1]

Life is a process. The process of seduction. At its best it is the spiritual seduction of man becoming God, at its worst and perhaps most humorous it is God becoming man. Spiritual

---

[1] I have never really been in control of my own baggage, and I have always sought out suspicious looking people, but they won't let you on the plane with those answers and if you have to lie to get on the plane it might not be the journey you should take. I think I will walk this one out, get there at my own pace and maybe appreciate the getting there as much as the being there or the being there more than I would have had I not gotten there just that way.

seduction is man becoming God: the rise. Corporal seduction is God becoming man. Each of these is a very big step indeed. God becoming man is a step which takes almost no effort because it is downhill, this game can take place at nearly 32 feet per second squared: acceleration maximum without outside force, and there is no outside force in this process.

Spiritual seduction is a path of steps, so many steps, each upward, each spaced just a fraction of a second in advance of the advancing, Rockette. Spiritual seduction is going against the grain on Earth back to where one really is. It is moving, without moving, reducing variables and learning how to do the most difficult thing for a person, to just let everything happen. It is letting go without releasing attention. It is continuing to have observation be the greatest level of influence. Any influence beyond observation is resistance.

As I swam through life I wanted to do the best I could be. As Edward Deming said, "Best efforts aren't good enough anymore." Not knowing much about his work I gleaned that part of his message is that everyone does the best that they possibly can and that doing the best that you possibly can just isn't good enough. I don't know that he went all the way from this clever premise to its ultimate extrapolation that the best effort is no effort at all and that life on Earth really isn't dependent on us, but that we are dependent on Life. We are dependent on Earth and anything else that we perceive ourselves not to be, hopefully in that order but typically not.

Spiritual seduction is the Everyday Path. It is the path that finds you: then leads you along. It is the path that when you have an idea of your own you stray from the path. It is a path of not doing and it is The Master Path. It is the shortest distance between here and nowhere and it intersects every other path that contains any truth. They intersect it because they are winding superfluously, providing diversions and switchbacks while the Everyday Path goes as straight as possible directly to your spirit.

Do the Great Smoky Mountains really look better if you have a bit of fudge in your mouth? Is romance really sweeter with or without a ring on that finger? Are you really going to get a better job than Bill Gates if you get a college education? Is the grass really greener on the other side of your next thought? Is there really no place like home and if so why doesn't somebody tell the travel agents and airlines that?

Seduction, as I have said, is the conversion of no to yes with Heisenberg looking on. Heisenberg taught us that observing something influences that which is observed, thus you couldn't really observe it you could only observe it under the influence of your observation. He taught us other things too, but we didn't learn those either. If you are bound to have influence then it only makes sense, to me, that the most life you can have would be having the most influence you could have. It turns out that having the most influence you can have is an aggressive drown. If you flail your hands around, kick your feet and scream as loud as possible you will be making the most disturbance that you can without ramming a commercial airliner into the World Trade Center or some other such brutal feat. Maybe, just maybe, we aren't supposed to be the greatest disturbance we can be. Maybe the game is to be the least disturbance we can while covering the most ground that we can. Maybe the least distance between two points is one point.

I spoke to an alleged friend of mine recently. An alleged friend because he is currently pretending to be a student of mine while I am washing my hands of him almost entirely and discovering a certain resistance I have to letting go of people. He is in the midst of a crisis, another crisis, he's counting. You are always trying to prove some aspect of either personal or fundamental philosophy. Personal philosophy being the study of how dumb you can get, fundamental philosophy having to do with how dumb you can make others.[2] Everything you do can be boiled down to something specific that you are trying to prove, don't know that you are trying to prove and that something doesn't taste the least bit like maple syrup. He, remember my alleged friend, was trying to prove that it is never too late to mess up one of your children. In a bid for most obscene act of the century his eighteen or nineteen-year-old (see facts) son was planning on getting married to someone fat and ugly before going overseas to fight in a war he didn't understand. Of course, there is always some war to fight in, of course, we never understand it, and if possible the war should be kept overseas. So, he was planning to marry someone he didn't even like so that if he got killed or maimed overseas he would be able to think of her in times of crises and realize that no matter how bad things got she wasn't there so things could always get worse. There is nothing like a future domestic war to make the current foreign war make more sense.

Dad: having several such notches in his belt and X's on the payroll realized the similarity between his son's behavior and his own. He headed out to save the son. He was going to talk some nonsense into "that boy" convincing him not to marry, at least not now. It was a long trip to where the son was, both geographically and psychologically. He didn't make it there but got as close as he could. I know that he wasn't too

---

[2] You are always either extrapolating or boiling down. Extrapolating is taking a single or very few cases and blowing them out to their sometimes logical extensions: erections. Boiling down is heating things up until all excess, what isn't necessary, has burned off and you are left with a little nugget just enough so that you can't swallow it only stand back awing. Extrapolating has the benefit of watering down so that one loaf and one fish provides inventory for a lot of fast food. Boiling down has what would have fed many feed very few. Neither approach works all by itself, applying both alternately with as little time as possible between results in a vertical perspective that should, at the least, give one pause, to collect what remains of oneself and start the process over.

close otherwise he wouldn't have had to shout so loudly for his son to try not to hear him, unless of course his son was hard of hearing him,[3] which he was, but not from some accident but rather a philosophical commitment to messing up, but he only seemed to be nearly deaf when some one other than his betrothed began speaking to him. Doesn't what seems to be love seem to be grand?

So dad arrived about as welcome as a real submarine in a bathtub and with about as much subtlety as Larry Flint and began his rush for salvation and liberation.

You may want to notice here that what the father was after wasn't really seduction but conversion. He was under the influence, and while under the influence (DLUI—driving life under the influence) he was attempting to drive not only his own life but his son's. Remember, and this is important, that the path down the drain is usually circular. There, now I just tried to do for your life, with that little piece of wisdom, exactly what the father tried to do for his son's and with about as much success. The father was the father, the son was the son and the Holy Ghost was momentum. Momentum is opening the future to the past without the presence of attention. The units of momentum are attention. (The units of attention are multiple illusionary perspectives per second—MIPpS.) Momentum is the lack of discovery that you can't get when from then without going through the present.

Dad arrived with a couple changes of clothes, running shoes, some half-baked ideas and fewer alternatives. He came ready to make a valiant, unsuccessful effort to save his son. His son would drown, of that he had no doubt but at least he would try and save him. What you must do in a case like this, and all cases where you attempt to interact with another person, is to

---

[3] Daughters are often hard of hearing her. They like to listen to their dads as Oedipus listened to his mom.

put something at stake yourself. If you want to be a stunt double for Joan of Ark(c)[4] you must be willing to fry in the process. A commitment to vegetarianism in such a situation just isn't an option.[5]

Dad had an option, one alternative to his son not getting married. The alternative was, again duhhhhhhhhhh, his son getting married. Have you ever noticed that when you have no options you like to pretend that you do and when you have options you like to pretend that you don't? It is this little bit of "this isn't it" that haunts us and until we can get rid of it, life won't really be all that it can be. (You may want to notice that the previous sentence contains the very violation it seeks to cure and that there is no word, yet, in the English language for this phenomenon but that there is in the Russian language— the word Russian itself.)

I am getting ahead of both myself and my story here and I apologize for that but hope that it is somewhere near as enjoyable for the gentle reader as it is for me to speed up to the point where things don't make any sense and then speed up some more to the point where they make sense again and then, at that precise point, rather than stepping back and enjoying how really clever I am and how much fun I am having, to move ahead even more rapidly from the point where they don't make sense to a line where they don't make sense then to a line where they do make sense. Then, not buying that line either moving to a geometric figure, simple or complex that doesn't make sense until it does, with even greater speed. Then, getting a box of crayons or really good colored pencils coloring in the figure in

---

[4] Imagine that kind of punishment for burning a steak.

[5] Phones: I believe deep in my heart that the dependents of Alexander Graham Bell should pay all of our phone bills. I also believe that the only reason that people ever go visit other people is so that they don't have to talk to them on the phone. Don't get me wrong, I think that life without the telephone would be intimate and rewarding.

such elegant tones as to make what is outside of the figure jealous of what is inside sufficiently so that I can finally step back and notice that what I have created is really only a hollow representation of what was there the whole time anyway and then I can smile the smile of one who has walked the whole road and gotten back home but with an appreciation of the journey during the journey and home while at home. Meaning: Dad is going to have to wait until the next chapter to teach you about family relations, pretended alternatives, burning at the stake, and spiritual seduction.[6]

---

[6] And Also Meaning: Pooh Bear was right about so many things and one of those was about how truly good condensed milk can taste, but he was wrong about eating it raw and I am right that if you boil the closed can of condensed milk for about an hour, then let it cool that upon opening it you will find something worth eating, but not too often and only in the face of being threatened by another chapter. (Should you be conservative you may want to spread it on graham crackers. But please try it, don't just think about it.)(This may be the only specific cooking recipe I include in this book so please consider it as such.)[6a] [6b]

[6a] (toenail) I never really trusted Rabbit. Rabbit seemed to be a cross between himself and himself, and if that isn't in breeding I don't know what is. Rabbit always seemed to have condensed milk but he never seemed to eat much of it and rabbit seemed, at least to me when I was little and now again when I am big, to have always liked Pooh Bear better than he liked himself and better than Pooh liked him. Don't get me wrong...

[6b] (second toe, toenail) If you cross Descartes, who I am quite sure crossed you by pretending to ass-ociate thinking with being, with the little engine who could, you get the mantra for condensed milk, "I think therefore I can." I am also fairly convinced that Descartes didn't get enough condensed milk or sweets in general, otherwise how could he have left us with such a bitter taste in our philosophy?

Life on the Tracks

Dad didn't have anything at stake. Don't ever trust anyone who has nothing at stake. They can behave any which way and without correlation between their actions and thinking. There is a precious zone of responsibility when the burden of proof is something that you can carry but it doesn't quite break your back. You need to care very much but not too much. If you care too much you become paralyzed maximizing your fear of influence, your own fear, and your own influence without extending your sphere of influence.[1]

Most people never discover this fear overtly but live under the influence. Each day, in their interactions with others, they thrill in the perpetually verified fact that nobody really listens to them. The fear I am speaking of is the one based on the hope that other people will do what you tell them to do and the knowledge that other people will always do what they do and what they do has little or nothing to do with you, and even less to do with what you say. You must continually, and this is well within the confines of the definition of being a human being, think that you have an influence and know that you don't

---

[1] You cannot take responsibility for anything inside yourself until you have taken complete responsibility for everything outside yourself. If you try and take responsibility for within without without first, you will define responsibility as burden, curtailing your ability to participate at a deeper level than pedestrian or blind advocate watchdog.

while thinking that you don't have an influence and knowing that you do. In other words, you must be so confounded that certainty seems the only place you can escape from thinking defined by polarities.

Dad cared more about what he had for dinner than he did about whether his son got married. Dad didn't know this and wasn't ready to find out. Dad had spent the previous weekend with a fat, ugly woman who pushed him around and who he didn't like. She had not yet decided whether he would have to marry her. (Sort of makes you wonder where the son got his patterns doesn't it?)

You have to watch for foreshadowing here or you will bump your head on it and never look at things the same. You will look at them more deeply, you will look at them in a larger time frame and for at least a while you won't like what you see as all you have missed rushes up at you for some badly needed attention. It seems that people used to be smarter than they are now. It further seems that part of that intelligence was a respect for the degree to which everything foreshadows something else. People used to understand that things were connected but have forgotten that in an attempt to prove that they really are interesting in a world of people who don't really care about anything but themselves. If a rabbit was this inattentive their race would be extinct and the very pot on the stove would be a rabbit trap with the rabbit sneaking into the house, like my daughter's cat, running recklessly but specifically toward the stove, skinning and gutting itself as it jumped toward the pot, landing in the stew pot and cooking to a golden brown just when you are hungriest. At the last moment the rabbit would utter the universal excuse for everything; "I don't understand." The stupidity defense. Isn't it odd that though you may not understand you can always misunderstand? Understand and misunderstand are not opposites, they are near misses, glancing blows that leave only psychological marks.

People seem to have become so scared that their own shadows chase them ever onward and the future is so daunting and the clues so missed that a kind of perpetual stupor guides life, if that can be called guided at all. I am trying to warn you here that the father's behavior was much like the son's and that the very solution to the specific problem at hand was not the obvious one of the son being less like the father, which the father would have said, but the father celebrating his current stupidity by flaunting it even more than he had in the presence of the son so that the son might, what the father could never do: catch on.

The father wasn't willing to give up anything in the process of rescuing his son. The purpose of certain floatation devices is to allow one to save the life of another without having to jump in the pot oneself. This way the father doesn't have to learn from the son's mistakes or his own but can save the son without getting his hands even the least bit wet, bloody or dirty. Now how likely is that? Please answer that question before you read on and ignore any bias I may seem to have regarding the answer. *Hint:* I think it is not bloody likely, just in case you wondered what not to react to. The father went to save the son but not to examine his own life. You cannot, must not, help another without helping yourself otherwise you blame them. You cannot love another without loving yourself. You cannot feed another without feeding yourself. You cannot mistreat another without mistreating yourself. Seduction is the perfect realization that everything is the same as everything else and the Everyday Path is the route to converting this realization to each cell on Earth.

The story indicates that Sir Walter Raleigh put his coat in a puddle so the fair young thing didn't have to get her feet wet crossing the puddle. Ignoring the political incorrectness of the entire situation and the tendency for women to want to have someone to blame for getting their feet wet, focus your attention for a moment on the fact that said Sir had actually borrowed the coat from his own wife and ponder the repercussions.

History is always a snapshot of where things stopped and it is always an attempt to prove something through deletion of something else. By ignoring Sir Walter Raleigh's wife's role in this whole event a lesson was learned that though neither true nor useful remains a permanent nick on the truth. The degree of scoundrel that knight was never comes to light. This leads to the number two rule of seduction: What seems to have happened didn't and what really did happen really didn't, thus, you can only learn what you wish to learn from what you think happened so you may as well liberally paint your history appreciating it all the while for the work of art that it is. Thus making history modern art, kind of a disturbed expression of then, rather than trying to make love to the woman with the photographic memory again in still life. If you paint a photograph you may as well just have started with a blank piece of paper: a tabla rasa.[2]

Dad wanted to stay as dumb as he was while teaching his son to get smarter.[3] Dad didn't want to learn but did want to teach. At this point, which seldom happens to a human being more often than sixty noticed times a minute, there needs to be a risk taken. Something needs to close off alleged alternatives. The importance of the situation should dictate the consequences. The more important the game played the more impor-

---

[2] It is safer and very useful to clean out the pan once you are done cooking with it. That way you can start with a fresh pan. This reduces the likelihood of disease and enhances the taste of the specific food you are cooking. With thinking you must calibrate to zero. You must clear out your thoughts, being reborn, possibility wise. Wisdom cannot happen when contamination happens between thought storms. Any good science requires a calibration back to zero. The test tube must be clean or it throws off the experiment. Any residue of past thinking contaminates your next thinking.

tant should be the consequences. There are only two things this father cared about in life: time with his sons (son's)[4] and his own ability to have sex. These two are not necessarily in the order of importance to him. You may want to consider other orders and in the process can't be as far off as I was, revealing that I really am trying to make this easier than it could be for your sake and am willing to sacrifice accuracy from time to time if need be just to cushion your inevitable rise.

Very simply put dad had to consider that if his son got married to this "human" he, dad, would have to either not see his sons for ten years or cut off his balls. Maybe both. With these as alternatives a whole range of excuses rushed out the proverbial back door and dad was on the hot spot even more than the groom. Without these possible futures the father would have exercised his one alternative which was to talk to the son and talk him out of getting married. If talking had worked in the past it isn't likely the son or the father would have been quite as stupid as they were now. The father wasn't seduced, there wasn't time for seduction, he was forced. He made up that the consequences of the marriage going on were so dire that he

---

[3] I once had a consultant come to consult with me. He was a specialist in Gardner's Model of Multiple Intelligences. He was sweeter than he was smart. He had read some of my books and wanted to meet me. After a delightful dinner I broke all my rules and attended his presentation at a local school. I watched the teachers in attendance trying to know and him teaching them that he knew. At the end of the evening I went up to him and asked him what he had learned that night. He got a silly look on his face, as though trying to think, and couldn't come up with anything. He said, "I will get back to you on that." I knew he wouldn't, and today, about eight years later, he has not gotten back to me yet. He was teaching about learning without learning himself.

[4] The son's also rises.

had to get clever, devious, fast, smart and successful or suffer at an accelerated rate.[5]

So, how do you stop your son from making the mistake of his life each moment when you really must stop him? Seduction takes time, so to have you learn seduction we must first alter your perception of time. One of the reasons that you are as busy as you are is because you don't know how to seduce and one of the reasons that you don't know how to seduce is because you are as busy as you are. The more often you interrupt yourself the more apt you are to take yourself less seriously and what you call self-esteem will lower while what self-esteem really is will rise but if this happens and happens often you will discover that the only reason the Titanic sank was because nobody was really having fun on it but trying to have fun and that trying to have fun just isn't the same as really having fun and that you can't fool Darwin when it comes to having fun.

Dad didn't want to lose his balls and didn't want to lose his son's, thus he couldn't keep his rationality. He wasn't quick enough to come up with the obvious solutions, nor, as I have said, was there time for seduction, so I had to tell him what to do.

The number one obvious reason for couples not to be couples anymore is what?

Infidelity.

Infidelity really has nothing to do with couples breaking up but it appears to be the number one reason that couples break up. "He cheated on me." "She cheated on me." Either of these phrases passes for just cause. The obvious solution to the father's ball dilemma was to marry the fat, ugly woman himself. That

---

[5] There is a lot to be said for suffering all at once and getting it over with rather than suffering a little bit at a time for a lifetime. Any perceived negative condition can pass much faster than it seems it can and leave more learning and less mark than you might imagine with an experience of resistance. In other words, if you won't always be this upset, why wait?

way he could both save his son and possibly learn what he needed to learn in the process. He needed to throw himself on the tracks, in front of the big, fat, ugly train. Short of this sensible solution he could have tried to bribe the bride (notice the similarity of those two words) not to marry his son. This might have worked had the bride already had money but her lack of wealth indicated a breach of appreciation for same, thus she was too poor to be bought. He had already tried to buy his son, with life, and hadn't succeeded.

So, he had two alternatives:: he could try and marry her or just have sex with her quickly and have the son find out. These are the only kinds of alternatives left to one in the absence of seduction. Would you rather learn how to seduce or be tortured endlessly by a short skinny German person with a point to prove and somewhat rotten teeth? Would you rather learn how to seduce or lose your balls? Would you rather learn how to seduce or go on with your life as usual having things getting slowly worse while thinking that they are getting slightly better? Would you rather learn seduction or be forced into a belief in reincarnation because this can't be all there is? Would you rather learn seduction or live a terribly painful life riddled with cancer, covered with warts and just out of arm's reach of a chocolate éclair: always? The choice is yours. If you are interested in seduction let's get started.

CHAPTER 4

Tender Gender

This buy polar existence is the source of energy on Earth and anything short of it is the offer of humor. You must balance out your head and heart. You must think precisely equal to the beat. Your thinking must dance to the beat of your heart, to do otherwise is to play musical chairs, a diminishing game where the best you end up is sitting down alone. The music will stop and you will be ready if you have been dancing plenty. If you are off balance a head you will figure out ways to worry about things that won't ever happen, or tether yourself to things that never did. If your body is leading you will be steeped in emotion until overdone, overwrought and unfairly tenderized past the point of re cognition. There must be a balance and there will be a balance. Any imbalance you get stuck on makes you precarious and gives you room for another argument with a scarecrow where it could have been a natural argument for perfection. Perfection is everywhere and you have to be sufficiently balanced to see it. If you don't have both feet on the ground it will knock you right over. You won't know what hit you, but it won't take you longer than a ten count to pull yourself up with some explanation.

The opposites feed you, but they stymie you too. They taunt you from both sides as you seek middle ground. You don't know what I will tell you next: You have to have all of your weight on one side and all of your weight on the other moving rapidly enough between the two that movement ceases, the teeter totter doesn't move because it thinks that it is balanced. Only consciousness near the speed of enlightenment can perform this feat, and it is no accident that the poles won't both fit in your head at the same time. It is not an accident that speed is your salvation, and it is also totally intentional that you can't think of anything at all when moving at light speed from side to invisible side. Lap-light swimming, the turns will drive you crazy but not nearly as nuts as the insanity that is stopping. Anything less than enough speed has you be eccentric and think one side is the winner. You reach for the arm to hold it up, indicating the winner, but just as you do flesh tears and you are on the other side with part of the winner.

It is supposed to be this way so that you move so fast that the moving can't make you motion sick. When you move too slowly you define yourself by the movement; when you move faster you can't stand it, but when you get fast enough, "Ah, yes, this is the life."

Any poles will do. Men and women, boys and girls anything less is howling at the moon, reigning cats and dogs instead of going all the way to people. Speed is the only way you will resolve the unresolvable. Too little speed and you end up married to someone you don't like or not married to someone you do like. Too little speed and you long for peace when you have war and war when you have peace. Aren't you dip lomatic?

MEN AND WOMEN, BOYS AND GIRLS

Women call it misogynism when men say it, feminism when women say it. Men call it the truth when they say it and wishful thinking when women say it.

I am the public offender, defending people's right to be deeper for freedom.

Spiritual Seduction

The problem with women is that they say yes physically at a very deep level and no mentally at every level. While this generates a profound amount of energy it also drives them nearly nuts. Especially in a world where men say okay at a deep physical level and okay at a mental level too. This looks, always, like indifference to the woman. She is stuck between her yes and no, the man doesn't want to talk, knowing without knowing, that talking is only trying to seduce her mental know, which is non-negotiable. She doesn't want to give herself physically because she thinks about it first. If she doesn't think about it first then the physical yes, a yes to vacuuming, a yes to dishes, a yes to doing and sex too, takes over and her mental no's go on the back burner for a while, or at least until her spouse is around. Then it is time to take a few no's out for a test drive. No's are always a way to assert power or find out if you have it. You never have it which is why you keep trying to assert it.

Women have been oppressed for thousands of years, which means that they have not been allowed to say no. The logical thing to do to cure this troublesome history is to learn how to say no. The logical way isn't always the wrong way, but in this case it is: too. Learning to say no is losing the body and heralding the mind. It is giving the mind what it thought it wanted. It doesn't give the mind a yes, that is nearly impossible, but it gives it the no it thought it wanted which puts the man genuinely ahead, instead of the figurative historical bust shot, should have been busted shot from the past. Men get ahead because women ignore their yes, stop with their no, and okay trumps no.[1]

---

[1] It is no accident that men called a bust the upper chest and head when it came to sculpture and a couple of milk bottles when it came to relationship. Okay looks advanced in the face of no. It looks pathetic in the face of yes. If women really want to be in control, and I hope they do for political, moral and because I always wanted to be treated like a sex object reasons, then yes and only yes is the way to do it.

Men are very low energy because okay yields no energy.

Men don't even care for sex, they inadvertently like everything else they do, then use sex to get to the women's yes which relieves them of the illusion that they are superior to women, which returns them to their rightful, in my case writeful, place as little boys aspiring to be mothered or successful and what is the difference?

Women are the power plans for energy on Earth, with their polar play. Many of them don't want to admit, submit, or adwit (*v.* **1.** a genuine acknowledgment with real humor **2.** the process of adding humor to anything) it either. So, they do the next logical wrong thing, they deny themselves sex in the name of denying the men sex. They deny themselves what they want and need in the guise of denying someone,,, the man, who really isn't interested, doesn't need it and considers getting his balls off on a long pass caught by a tight end on any given Sunday,, what he doesn't care about.

I used to think that a woman saying no to something meant something about the something. Now, wiser, I know that it means more about her.[2]

With a woman there are nearly never intentional no's. They are all accidents culturally dictated. Men's okays are all accidents too, at least at a personal level. Don't take it personally, I just had a few no's to get out and you happened to be in the right place at the wrong time. You are always at the right place at the right time when women are tuned to their physical yes. You are forced into the spiritual or at least

---

[2] People always say yes when they can. Men say okay when they can't say yes, women say no when they can't say yes. Nostalgia is longing for a time when you said yes.

a much higher earthly orbit just by the sheer trans parent yes of it.[3]

Men have walked on the moon, but they haven't yet admitted that they have no evolutionary significance without the yes only available from a woman. They cannot admit and can only sarcastically adwit that they are worse than nothing, a mere distraction, without it.

Playing leapfrog with slugs, while making you pretty cocky at first, won't really be much fun after long. It will get you slimy and it won't get you any closer to the Slug Olympics.[4]

What I have been explaining above is really the roots of the odd attraction between men and women. The men need the yes but the women can't find it.

When one is physically fertile and mentally sterile the highest state that can be reached, the culmination of life, and the kickoff to the postpartem blues is giving birth (women).[5] When one is semi-fertile mentally and semi-fertile physically and can't

---

[3] When parents say yes children become teachers. When parents say no they become dictators and the kids become semi-creative parrots. You need to be very careful with a child because children will almost always forgive you before you have learned what you needed to learn. An adult will usually not forgive you until long after you have learned and forgotten what you needed to learn and practice, giving you plenty of room to defend yourself when you don't even remember what you did. And they say: "Diamonds are forever."

[4] There is a Slug Olympics but nobody has arrived at it sufficiently on time to have it held. It goes down in history with one of my other dead ideas, The Herpes Hall of Fame. There is nothing much lonelier than a monument to a disease that nobody wants to admit that they have.

[5] Birth is a metaphor for yes. It is one way the woman is forced to say yes. The greatest human expression of yes, for both sexes, is death. Nobody says no to death for too long. The more yeses you have said in your life the easier time you have dying, and the longer life you will lead, and follow.

even get preggy the culmination of life is a touchdown on Earth (men).[6] The resolution isn't only that women need to become more philosophical but that men need to learn to speak.

The resolution is clear: Women have to be more like women and men have to be more like women, and they all have to enter into the joyful,,, foreplay-ridden and sexually-expressed adventure of gaining the, hopefully, but not often, demilitarized zone between no and yes. In other words: They have to unite in the tender wrestling match of seduction.

The Cure: You Just Have To Have Sex Here.

You have to agree upon where the truce talks will begin. They have to be held somewhere embarrassing for both sides so, the obvious interim solution is sex, the physical manifestation of conjunction and conflagration of the otherwise loosely spun cloth of the emperor's clothes. There is no sex in Heaven,[7] and not because the people don't want to but in Heaven everybody is super fertile but all the newcomers come from Earth so there is an ordinance against sex. There isn't one on Earth, so you can stop pretending that there is. You are supposed to get it here. The only way we can get on with spiritual seduction is to have successful worldly seduction. There really is no sex in Heaven and there is a shortage of good sex here: so, what are you waiting for? The only way you can discover your real purpose in life is to cut through the diversions, the labors, the problems and above all the frustrations of life. These aren't really of life, they are of death. Many people, while claiming to have good sex, will, when pressed with their clothes on, admit that they experience frustration around sex or more often the absence of

---

[6] The touchdown here could be a football metaphor but when foot meets ball it usually is painful so let's just mean a returning to our senses. A coming back from moon gazing for a little and really looking at what is here. That is the first step in men moving from okay to yes.

[7] You may wonder about my source on this one.

sex. Sex can be the most embarrassing human act; it can also be the most incredible. It can be birth without the baby.

When you are having sex regularly and experiencing orgasms very often you will discover that, though the marketers would have you think differently, sex really isn't what you want. Sex isn't frustrating you. What frustrates you is deeper. What frustrates you is a lack of seduction. What frustrates you is not discovering yourself as a creature of yes. If you think you are a mean nasty person in a mean and nasty world and you have a cold you may think that the cold caused you to be a mean and nasty person. The more prevalent a condition the more apt it is to be blamed for nearly anything. Most people live with an irreconcilable difference: I want sex but I don't get it, at least not often enough.

You have to be getting a lot of sex, much more sex than you think you deserve before you can even entertain the idea of good sex. Even a starving Frenchman usually doesn't criticize the food; a starving woman does but only if the cook is a man, a woman or herself.

As long as you don't have something you can blame that something for something else, creating a chain of blame leading away from who you really are to no place you really want to go.

You must have so much sex, sex and sex and more sex. You get to act like a person just out of the desert, finding a Kool-Aid stand with all you can drink free. After a while and many wild acts you will have answered the quantity question which, as always, rolls over presenting its underbelly, the quality question. You will have enough instances, enough variation determine not only good sex from bad sex but 132.352 exquisite sex from 132.355 exquisite sex. You don't have to be an accountant to have good sex, but it doesn't help. You will be able to discriminate, you will turn your back on everything less than a certain point and you will raise that point. You will have enough experience to, with great accuracy, extrapolate what is beneath your standards and not partake. Along with this skill you will continually raise your standards discovering the kissing-cousin-nearly-incestuous-relationship between quantity and quality. There is a specific context-dependent modifier which sets the ratio of quantity to quality. The equation determines the market price for how much quality time equals how many quantity times. The discovery of this ratio sets one free from constraints of Earth and prepares one for spiritual seduction.[8] It is the key to unlocking the mind-prison that most people only get glimpses outside of.

When you have cracked the equation between quality and quantity you have stopped time guaranteeing that you no longer have to be so busy just to survive. In fact, you only have to do something once to complete everything there is. Everything is a metaphor for everything else and every instance is a metaphor for every other instance; when you can put numbers to the metaphor you will have cracked the great riddle of just what is worth doing and what isn't. But– – –we aren't quite there yet, though on the way. To get there, remember, you have to have all the sex you want with anyone you want. You need to end all denial and open completely to what seems to be the opposite sex. To get all the sex you want and increase the amount of sex you want you will need to seduce. The process of seduction in the sexual domain on Earth is called flirting. With flirting you pussythigh around a no rather than taking it

---

[8] To get at this ration you have to do a little sexual math. You have to find someone you really like and think that you can't have. You need to find someone else that you might be able to have but aren't nearly as attracted to. You then work out an economy based on how many times you would have to have sex with number 2 to equal sex with number one once. This kind of economy is useful and sets up entirely the relationship between quantity and quality so necessary for the newest oldest profession to become love with sex rather than prostitution.

straight on and get to be a witness to that no moving closer to a yes or more to a no but moving. Flirting is a vital step on the way to seduction because it allows you to play unilaterally with others. It allows you to flow without getting damned and it allows you to have everything be practice rather than being so darn serious. We will get to seduction, but we will flirt with getting there. Now, on your way to more sex than anyone has ever had on Earth before, let's explore the wonderful world of the Everyday Path as foreplay for life. Seduction on Earth clears the way for spiritual seduction.

It's a lottery. The odds aren't set here or in advance. You may as well play, exploring the yes and the no of it. It isn't about you, but when you learn your power to convert no to yes you will be at the heart of the game.

CHAPTER 5

Flirting: The Lost Art

Sitting on the front porch, an old house in Houston, though it could have been anywhere, I sat on a wicker chair optimistically holding my weight, trying to grasp hers. Next to me, "the pessimistic chair," the perpetual "no," the little blond girl with little gold earrings much younger than her years in every regard but craziness. I was in love, she smelled so good. I had just met her a few days before. I had expressed the love thousands of times in my head but not once, to her, out of my mouth, an imbalance so delicate that my heart raced. I didn't want to love her forever, we had no future, but I certainly wanted something very specific from her. I wanted what most men tend to pretend that they want from women but rarely do.[1] I did.

She wanted to remain crazy and I was driving myself insane. Her earlobe caught my attention forever, her elbow, under the thin light blue sweater. It was too early to focus on any of her body parts described scientifically as intimate. I didn't have a chance but I had to go for it. My intention was to express the love and make love in ever-advancingly intimate forms. Her

---

[1] Every once and a while a man really does want sex. About as often as he wants to explore calculus in his spare time. You may not believe me, but you can prove it to yourself. If a man doesn't get sex there will be the men's equivalent of an emotion, usually anger, then he will get on with something else and forget about sex entirely. That isn't what someone does who really likes something. In sex men always lose.

intention, I can only guess, was to have me be a dipstick to find out answers to the following questions, though she wouldn't really put them to bed, or me, once I answered them: "Isn't my hair nice? You can't have it." "Aren't I cute? You can only look but not touch." "Wouldn't you like to have me? You can't." "Aren't I lucky that he likes me, he should like me, aren't I lucky that I don't like him, isn't he ugly and aren't I cute?" If firemen were to attempt to put out a very relevant fire, say their pornographic collection or TV Guide was about ready to be consumed in flame, they could not have found a more effective fire retardant or fighter than the thoughts in her head. I was still on fire; I was burning with desire to match her indifference. One of us would win and I had to find a way for it to be both. There is, after all, some communication between the surface of the ocean and those little creatures, at great depths with little lights on their heads, little blondish lights. I focused my little light on her lower throat, that soft place where the angle of the skull-esophagus has turned into the flat plains leading to the mountains below but not nearly there yet. It was so flat, so tempting, so ready, waiting for me, virginal, unmapped by anyone who cared.[2] I have always wondered, well maybe not when I was a little kid or in church, but I have often wondered if losing virginity counts if one is not present at the moment. I am inclined to vote for that it doesn't, though I suspect there are other candidates equally qualified running. If virginity is a state of mind we can combine spirituality with sexuality and rise to a sexual angelic expression rather than the down and dirty, near flatulent expression that most sex is in its lack of entirety (meaning consciousness isn't present, "There were no witnesses, to your honor or loss of it."—Honest Judge).

---

[2] Have you ever noticed that there is no man more caring than the one who wants something, however fleeting?

I drew in a breath, exhaled, closed my senses to the conversations in her head, felt a slight smog driven breeze on my face and touched her shoulder with three fingers of my right hand. There was a bone there. The beginning of sexual anatomy class. She didn't seem to notice the touch, I swooned. To say that she was insensitive is to give insensitivity a bad name. She was as oblivious as a man. I realized that there was a possibility that if we had sex she wouldn't know it. Virginity?

Flirting is taking liberties without asking for them. It is reaching across alleged boundaries without asking permission and being very attentive to both reaction and invitation. Flirting is trying something that you don't know if you will get away with and backing off if you don't get away with it and moving ahead to the next obvious try if you do get away with it. Flirting is exploring new terrain a little tiny piece at a time and monitoring the consequences at each step of the way.

One of the major benefits of flirting is that it allows people to split things into ever smaller pieces, increasing the number of things that one can attend to, in the process increasing the accuracy with which one perceives anything. Flirting is dismantling no, slowly. I knew that I had three fingers on her shoulder: in a non-flirting situation, which I hoped this wasn't, I would have only known that I touched her. Flirting increases sensitivity.

Staying present while going somewhere new is about as fun as life gets. Taken from either side, the first touch of a breast is worth attending to. From the man's perspective he slowly works his way around to the breast beginning with "hello" and finally getting to squeezing the entire breast with the nipple between the thumb and middle finger while gauging if she likes it and just how hard.[3] The more awake you can be in this process, this progression toward intimacy, the more fun you will have and

---

[3] This stage is usually praying: getting what you prayed for and thanking God.

the more fully you will have opened yourself to another person, which is really the point. From her perspective: you know what he wants, you know that he is coming, you know that his fingers on your shoulder are a temporary R and R in a demilitarized zone. You know that he wants more; you know that you may or may not want more. You are afraid that he might want too much more and afraid that he might not want enough more. I overheard a very attractive cheerleader in high school say, "I hope he knows where to put it after a few days." Either she was referring to the new and first male cheerleader and his pom poms or she was making a comment on the standard dilemma between every male and every female in the mystory of the planet. Mystory is personal history. The larger your mystory, the more curious you will be.

And, I wondered whether I would know where to put it in a few days. The key to knowing where to put it in a few days and in how many days to put it there and to enjoying the whole process of seduction is flirting. To flirt effectively you must be bold enough to take just the precisely right sized step and be mature enough to accept the consequences of that step or sell that step to the other person. To seduce, to change no to yes, you will need to synchronize your biological clocks. You will need to let the other person know just when to move and just how much. You will have to be pleasantly surprised, not react- ing, when they know even better than you do now what you like.[4] You must open to this possibility and become a magnet for just such a person. Generic flirting successfully is receiving no just about forty-nine percent of the time. Successful personal flirting is based on the acceptance and declination rates of the two or more people involved. In other words: What is the half- life of a no and how long is a yes held open? To what degree can

---

[4] It is somewhere between victim and martyr that the human race is lost or won, lost or found, ignored or celebrated.

you generalize a yes or a no? In even other words: Would the woman be willing to have sex in return for the boy-scoutish-crossing-the-street services rendered? Would a "thank you" suffice or should there be some payment in kind? What is the exact right return on investment to keep attention peaked while not being so little it turns to boredom or so much that it turns to overwhelm?

I kissed her twice before dinner. Each time took more bravery than I had, almost. Each time I met a conspiracy of non-responding upper and lower. Each time she didn't give the odd little look of disbelief that it would have taken to cool me off. You can't fail, you can just quit too soon, or not soon enough. Oddly both of these can seem like failure. After dinner, dinner was a kind of delicious confused mix of something with spaghetti sauce and the company of a blonde who knew less what was going on than the other two at dinner: and me gushing, exuding love from every pore.

A secret: It wasn't love for her. It wasn't love for her thin muscular legs, for her slender wrists, for her defensive and completely humorless demeanor. It was love because I could. It was love because it was in me and needed to get out. It was love because I couldn't hold it inside one more moment. I had just finished leading a course, a course where love had to be limited however slightly. Have you ever been to Niagara Falls, the perfect place to get divorced? There is never an object to love; love is inclusion. Love doesn't determine what to include. If you doubt me on this one, remember one thing and try another. Remember that what you have called love in the past, for the most part, probably isn't what I am talking about. What I am calling love is what you will experience as a threat to your continued existence once you can seduce anyone anywhere anytime: please leave this particular blonde off your list: just kidding, her number is 706.754.7540, you have nothing to lose.

Try saying, "I love you" to someone. Then try saying, "I love." If you try this a few times you will discover that "I love" is much more accurate than "I love you." "I love you" is always some degree of fetish, an alias, as you confuse something that really originates and runs full cycle inside you with something outside you. Yes, you can love anything and anyone, and further yes you already do.

After dinner, full now of food too, I kissed her again. Maybe the girl was hungry, she kissed back. She kissed more than back; she almost knew she was kissing. The rewards of flirting come when they do, never predictably. They are a random train arriving at the station just when you really needed one because your foot was already reaching for the step and you were almost late for arriving early as usual. What happened between the first two kisses and the "better" one? I have no idea nor do I care. I don't want her to be predictable;[5] if she is predictable I lose interest; so there is no need to flirt. I made pictures of doing other things to her that night, just to give her a hint.

---

[5] The faster you get the less you will be able to avoid predictability and the absence of appreciation of patterns by others will be enough to drive you to éclairs or movies all by yourself.

CHAPTER 6

More Flirting

If you are laying siege to the castle and it looks to be a long campaign, you may want to pace yourself a little bit. You may want to attack just from nine to five, with an hour for lunch. The question then becomes, "What do you do with your evening?" Flirting takes you apart. It does so in such a nice way with such excitement and in such great company that sometimes its deep effects aren't noticed. What did they do in the evenings in the old days when there were castles and there were blatant sieges?

They made up games. They had challenges with each other for who could throw a spear the farthest or who could hit the hardest. They gambled wildly with games of chance. They set up games that would be much shorter than the siege and had the all important elements of having people find out fairly quickly if they won or lost. In short: They rebuilt their worth as human beings in games where even if they lost they won because they got some measurement of where they stood. As a human being you are engaged in a lifetime siege, you attack the castle, of self and more, each day hoping that this is the day it falls but with fingers crossed hoping it doesn't because the status quo siege seems more safe than the unknown one that might follow. You need interim games; you need ways to measure how you are doing in the absence of big game feedback. You need feedback quite regularly or you forget who you are and what you are doing. Flirting gives you that blessed feedback.

Spiritual Seduction

You walk up to the register at the grocery store. "Can I have this box of Hamburger Helper for ten cents off because it doesn't have any hamburger in it?" Or because you saw a coupon in the paper for ten cents off something that made you think of Hamburger Helper. Then you shut your mouth and wait for the cashier to respond. Who knows, you may end up talking to the manager and he may decide that what they really need is a new spokesperson for Hamburger Helper and you are it and you get put on national TV advertising a product that you wouldn't eat if they paid you. Who knows, you may end up married to the cashier or the person who was behind you in line. Who knows, the cashier might just say no.[1] Who knows? "Who knows?" (Who knows?)[2]

There are three parts to a flirt: There is the parry, which is you reaching out to the other person, there is their defense or offence in relation, hopefully, to that parry and there is the waiting to find out what their response will be.[3] The waiting is really the hardest part though the parry will be difficult for those who have defined themselves as shy or introverted and the response will seem to be the most difficult for people who have pretend self-esteem or mock energy. They will be tempted to defend themselves against something, anything, often before the response even comes, revealing that the people who pretend to be most secure really are least secure and can't stand

---

[1] Remember, most people have a no ready like gunslingers of old had a gun ready. It isn't personal, they have their quota of no ready and if you diminish it just even by one you have done them and the planet a service.

[2] Who knows?

[3] The parry sort of sets the stage or sets the table, it gets things going and is the hardest part before you do it and the easiest part afterward. The offense or defense includes the most temptation because you want to respond, but if you do then it is no longer flirting it is just you hooked. The waiting is really the hardest part because you really have to leave what happens up to another trusting yourself to weather the storm.

the spaces in life which are substantially more plentiful than either the notes or the rests.

Back to the castle. What do the people inside the castle under siege do at night? They don't play games and gamble because they can't. They don't have the option of perceiving the siege as optional because they are allegedly home. The siegers can call off the attack and go home; this is what keeps them sieging. The people in the castle are home so they can't hold out the hope that home will be better; home is just this way. The people in the castle will do one of two things, sometimes a mixture of both. They will either think about how awful it will be when they lose the battle or how mediocre it will be if the siegers quit: OR they remember: they remember how wonderful life was, it wasn't, though there is nothing like a hard time now to clean up the past, when they were not under siege.[4]

So the people in the castle who are under siege yield, they wave the white flag and, in their leisure, which is the only time that really counts toward quality of life, they leave the present and move to the past, remembering, or to the future, hoping or worrying. They have left the castle, they are having no fun, they would have more fun if they laid siege to the castle themselves. Why did they build a castle in the first place? Anything you build is something that you may and probably will have no fun defending. The only good life is an offence in a sea of less than good lives. People who suffer together suffer together.

---

[4] I am in favor of a new law I just made up that people should have to bob for problems. To find out how much fun this can be, if you haven't and even if you have, fill up a 400 gallon container with water. Place several good quality, big apples on the surface. Hey, they float. Then try to pick up an apple with your mouth not using any other part of your body. If problems were harder to get we would all have many of the same sort of problems, not enough problems. Wouldn't that be fun? We could work together on common problems rather than spending almost all of our time being problems for each other. Heck, if we really got along God or some alien might come down to visit and show us just how alike we really are in the face of real difference.

Spiritual Seduction

Flirting has you experience being the one performing the siege of the fortress of no rather than defending yourself. If you are defending yourself you have already lost. If you are flirting you can move ahead, you can risk what you have, finding out what you have in the process. You will not risk, for long, what you don't have because that kind of bluff just doesn't hold up in the heat of battle.

A rule: It is always more fun to flirt than not to flirt. Another rule: Life is even better when you reach the anvil or flamethrower no than when you aren't flirting.

You can flirt when someone tells you that you are wrong. You can look right at them, cock your head like the RCA dog and say, "Really?" thinking, and this is the important part, that you might be wrong and you might not. If you really think that they will have to rethink their attack making you the attacker and them the castle. If you know that you aren't wrong you have to start paying rent on the castle.

There is the basic kind of flirting which has sexual over and undertones but there are many other types of flirting. Flirting always entails having at least one more part curiosity than certainty. There are ways to increase your curiosity and if you know them you can't use them (because you would be stuck in knowing again). I will hint at a few of these very soon but I think that you are getting the idea that it is better to live outside the castle than in it and that is exactly the little bit of possible knowing that will be useful as you undertake the nearly Herculean task available, and well worthwhile, that you will learn in the chapter called "Flirting With Seduction."

PUTTING OUT

Putting out means giving not extinguishing, though it can mean both. Putting out is also a golf term which means finishing the hole without attending to the rebellious and seemingly stupid rule that whoever is farthest from the hole shoots first. Try that in other areas of life and find out how it works, really.

Most people think that they want more in return than they give: they do think that but they don't want it. If you get more in return than you give then you increase your attention, the container for attention being self-esteem, thus the self-esteem must be greater. Your surroundings must match your self-esteem, your life must get better. Keeping a high self-esteem well-fed requires a very big life in deed. Most people would rather reserve their opossum rights than take such risks. Flirting was invented so that you didn't have to take such risks all at once.

Flirting is fifty percent art and fifty percent science. Art in that it applies freely everywhere and is objective; science in that it is ever smaller and completely subjective. The deeper you look the larger the art and the science parts become. Flirting is the most honest game that human beings can play. Flirting breaks down all fences and unloads all guns; it defuses all bombs and opens all crotches. If you are a bit shy and bashful you may first have to flirt with flirting. You may have to try things theoretically before you try them with your body. You may need to write fiction until nonfiction shows up. You may have to try touching a tree first and a person later. You can work your way up, microbiology is flirting with such beasts as amoebas, from there you move up species wise to the wisest species of them all, God, which is spiritual seduction. When you garner enough of God's attention you are really in trouble; you are playing poker with life and death stakes. Playing with protozoa it is usually the protozoa's life at stake and not your own. To have flirting teach the most in the least period of time and be the most fun, you have to risk that which you don't think you can afford to lose and go for that which you don't think you deserve to have. Did I mention that she was very cute and blonde? Did I mention that she had very large but attentive breasts, breasts that chal-lenged me because I am seldom mature enough to go after any-thing but small ones? I grew up in Wisconsin and still I get embarrassed driving by a herd of cows. I will conquer this, I will conquer this, I will conquer this; at least I will have fun trying.

If you don't get a no you aren't flirting. That night with her I got one no. I asked her to sit on my lap; I knew she wouldn't, but I just had to find out what getting a no would be like. There was no need to push too hard because there was plenty of time. I got more than I expected and rather than rushing onward I accessed the three months until we would meet again and went for just enough to excite me and delight me for that period of time so that I would be ready for the next meeting and the next advance. If I had touched her breast that first night it would have cost me. She wasn't ready and I wasn't ready. There is nothing much worse than bad sex and there is nothing much better than good sex.

Flirting opens the door to everything being foreplay and if it is done well enough it is a sufficient win for all involved that it doesn't need to lead anywhere. Flirting is to play as leaves are to trees: if you get my meaning.

You need to flirt with each person you meet. You need to delicately and sometimes boldly find their no's.[5] Not their full blown, grown-up, mean and nasty no's. You need to find their baby no's their toddler no's. You need to find the no's that cutting them off at the past doesn't spite their face. You need to find the no that has not yet been fully identified with who they are. You need to find the no that does not yet have a legal or historical precedent. You need to find the no that didn't just

---

[5] Touching their no's with your eyes closed is a sign that you have not flirted enough, in other words, you are sober which is a state that is not com-patible with flirting. Flirting is both inebriating and addictive, it is also good for you. It contains way more than the minimum daily requirement of all essential vitamins.

win the last election for most important idea of the month. The only way you will find these little no's is to move in tiny increments. The only way you will find them is to always have just a little more at risk than you dare. If you risk too little you go to sleep; if you risk too much you gain evidence that you never should have played. You need to find those places in them and you where the no is created but not yet weaned. Where it can still be negotiated with but is observably there. You need to play with the person's soul.[6]

You get to look at each moment on Earth as an opportunity to flirt. You can flirt with your new boss in his first group meeting, you can flirt with the checkout person in the supermarket, you can flirt with your spouse, with your children, with your teacher, with yourself, with your pets, with your food, with your silverware, with your stomach, with your reading, with your self-esteem, with your butcher, baker and mother. You need to flirt everywhere. I need to end this chapter.

Soon. I just flirted with ending. I got to the no, the end of the chapter, but then it wasn't quite the end. Flirting is interrupting your no's and any little no's you find. Flirting is legal in all fifty states and any provinces, you may want to try it in. Flirting is a necessary step to seduction. It is the baby steps of converting no to yes. Please, please, please, try several little flirts with things or people, depending on your current

---

[6] Soul is the smallest unit of measurement that a person is currently able to perceive. You get deeper, as a human being, as you are able to derive greater entertainment from smaller and more subtle things. A nuclear power plant is a master of atoms; you are supposed to be the master of the universe. You are supposed to be able to split anything into smaller pieces and extract the energy that was holding it together for your own use. You are a human electro power plant and movement of soul is the generator. Flirting has you be able to attend to ever smaller things revealing the soul connection between yourself and another. The roots of successful relating are deeply rooted in a commonality in the perception of what size chunks and how many constitute a meal shared.

evolutionary stage before you go to the next chapter and regale yourself with many examples of flirting.

Did I mention that flirting is the cheapest, easiest and least painful way to raise your self-esteem and enjoy your life more? If I already did it bears repeating, if I didn't since it does, please read the following: Did I mention that flirting is the cheapest, easiest and least painful way to raise your self-esteem and enjoy your life more?

Legendary Apes I Have Dated

In my PBS special *Legendary Apes I Have Dated*, I explore the implications of knocking down the barriers between similar species, like men and women, only to discover that the contribution that flirting has made through history has been second only to the implicate order of things and the status quo.

Do you have any idea how rutted in dogma the status quo is? Do you have any appreciation for how often you not only don't do what you want to do but don't even know what you want to do because your personal ability to flirt has been overridden by a social, non-oral inhibition and restriction of the exploration of the grass on the other side of the street? Well, if you don't let me tell you: a lot.

The only reason you go after the castle is because life in your own castle isn't so great. The only reason you buy new things, that you don't really need, is because your delusion is nearing complete that your neighbor has better sex, brighter kids, more fun and an overall quality of life better than yours. If the shoe fits wear it and if you are wearing it nobody else can, so the first one to the fastest shoe may well win the next race. If you don't see almost all of life as a competition in which you not only aren't winning but haven't got a chance then you aren't really paying attention. If you just don't think you are that competitive then I urge you to just sit, or run around like a worker bee doing a lot, and being fairly well-convinced that you aren't getting anywhere near out of life what you could. That things aren't turning out the way you would like or the way you have planned are fighting words and just because you don't have the whatever it takes to attack the castle straight on, that doesn't mean you don't take a swipe, a holler or a righteous injustice anytime you can. Just because you aren't the designated hitter doesn't mean that you aren't in the game and that you haven't been seen toting a battering ram from pet show to pet show from time to time.[1][2][3]

Let me tell you: If you can't enjoy the process of finding the treasure it won't be one. The process of finding the treasure is flirting. You need to flirt, and you need to have something generally specific to do, which you won't, should you find yourself in the castle under siege, which you will. It seems the purpose of most cultural advances is to make the world a substantially less friendly place. This makes sense, at some level, and fits well into the mass marketing overview where the final objective is to turn everything you don't want into a want and everything you already want into a need and everything you need into a fact and every fact into some artifact of your physique. I get the idea that I am

---

[1] Traces of discontent have been found in the marrow of all suburban homo-sapien bones, with somewhat heavier residue in those of women than of men which explains why women live longer than men. They aren't in any hurry, God bless them, to die that discontent: or without a few more years of discontent. My grandmother genuinely liked my grandfather, weren't those the good old days?

[2] I am noticing some cynicism here and I don't even like it a bit. I urge you to cut it out because cynicism is a little too much like too sharp a knife at a "how to control your anger" convention, or really good close-up glasses at a Mary Kay convention. If you have ever tried to peddle your most recent joke book at a CPA convention or smoked at a CPR convention you know what I mean.

[3] I am fairly convinced that by the next chapter I will be able to find just the right person with a just sharp enough knife to cut my tongue from my cheek with a minimal amount of pain. I have always been optimistic.

not digressing sufficiently enough to be fully misunderstood here. Let's take a shortcut in the form of a trick:

The Trick: You will, from time to every time, get upset. When this happens there is a simple cure, the cure is curiosity. For nearly every disease there is some cure and some symptoms. For the symptoms of "this isn't it-ness" manifesting itself as any degree of positive or negative upset, the cure is always the same. As I pointed out in the last chapter curiosity is the major element of flirting. It is major because curiosity requires a kind of turning inside out. Curiosity is showing your hand to the other players and finding out what they will do when they "know." In other words: Putting them in the castle of knowing which is always and perpetually, imperpetuitously under siege. Other people and other things, anything other than who you perceive yourself to be, seeks to supplant any self-knowledge that you have by having you take the ever defensive position by having you know something about it. If you know something about it you are stuck with it. The degree of bias in your knowledge is substantially less relevant than the "fact" of your having unsaid knowledge. When such knowledge gets said it is an assault, when it goes unsaid it is a hiding place. In the same number of words: When such knowledge gets said it is the siege, when it goes unsaid it is the castle. Knowledge is like a hot French-fry: well almost.[4]

You are nearly always under attack; your sovereignty as an autonomous human being is challenged by somebody at work asserting that you look nice today. They want to have what

---

[4] I grew up around Chicago. The wind would rip off the lake sufficiently that if someone lived there from toddler times they would defend, adjust, by adding a four degree lean into the wind to balance off its effect. While these people looked smart and even balanced as the wind blew, on a calm day they were unsettled and unsettling. You may not want to carry your armor with you everywhere you go; there are just some places, most places, it will get in your way. Oddly, should you leave your defenses at home though you will have ignored the truly American Express advice and left home without it, you will have a better time than ever which virtually makes you immortal.

they say be true, so they say the stupidest things. They want you to buy what they say wholesale, thinking you are getting a deal when all you are really getting is a version of their problem. They want to, in the process, covertly convert themselves to being the expert in your appearance, which, to them, is your life. None of this may seem sinister but by the time these polite attacks have found your every waking and sleeping moment you become susceptible to any input at all. You bow to adjectives thrown at you by anyone, worshiping the opinion of those hinted to be more fortunate than you. The test is when they say something negative. If a cloud appears in your sky and you decide that since they were right all those times before about your looking nice they must be right this time too? No, you just pay the bill. You knuckle under thinking that what they said really means something about you. You either defend the castle or condemn yourself to leaving the present because you don't really look nice in it anyway.[5]

You are almost never in the present but usually when you are there is either not a mirror around or you don't know to look in it. In the present you don't really know anything at all. That is one of the reasons your muscles don't hold any tension, your jaws relax and a gentle smile hides your canines. Did you ever wonder why your wisdom teeth came out so late, are stored in the back of your mouth and are often pulled? Think about it if you still have them.

You are almost never in the present and there is only one "real" human upset: the loss of the present. The purpose of every siege is to get you to give up the present much like the purpose in the game "King of the Hill," or employment-wise "King of the Mill."

---

[5] If you don't really look nice then you aren't in the present. In the present you look the best you ever will.

If you are good at seduction there need be no bloodshed. The castle becomes a park in which everyone gets to experience the wonders of their nature. You are always seducing or being seduced. If you can get them to melt in your mouth you won't ever need to use your hand. Everybody has a thin candy shell and it would always surprise you how really thin and how really candy it is. You get seduced by someone defining their relationship to you as one of authority by saying things either that you can't resist or must resist; either way you are a goner, leaving the present. The cure, as I have said, is curiosity. Each time and every time that someone or something attempts to define your world you must get curious about something. If you could catch an arrow shot at your heart wouldn't you be the lucky one? Wouldn't you look awfully good, in practice not theory, standing there with the arrow in hand and your heart in tact, them with the bow as evidence and you more than willing to receive another arrow for your collection should they have the gall to nock and pull another one?

So they say, "You didn't get the papers in on time." You reply, with curiosity, "When were they due?" A magical thing happens. The attention that they attempted to direct to you goes back to them. They sought to force your focus onto yourself and it ended up back on them. You are a mirror; they a boomerang. "You are late." "What time did you expect me?" "You never hug me anymore." "Would you like a big juicy fat hug right now?" "We never talk anymore." "What?"[6] "If you loved me you would take the garbage out." "Aren't you taking yourself a little seriously?" "You don't love me anymore." "How could I show you that I love you?"

---

[6] Remember that almost always if the person says that you never talk anymore they mean that you don't listen. If they say you don't listen they mean you don't talk. In the land of illusion nothing is as it seems and there are a lot of seams where rips and tears and imperfections have been stitched together by hand or moth.

Some of these are just examples, some unjust. The difference is whether they apply in your particular situation. All attacks are assertions. Declining the attack always takes the form of a question asked with genuine, as close as you can get, curiosity. You have to have the courage to muster curiosity because when you do you come from not knowing. Not knowing is always more powerful than knowing. Knowing always comes from weakness, always, every time, even this time. If you are present you can say yes; if you aren't you must either no or know.

At an early age youth came naturally to you so did curiosity; you explored freely. You played. At a later age you wondered seriously where curiosity went. Curiosity became a threat to you and your status quo; this is a condition called work. You are either busy maintaining and defending the status quo or overthrowing it. The status quo is your current castle. The status quo is never present; curiosity brings you closer to the present. Curiosity seeks knowledge, flirts with knowledge, without ever getting there. Knowledge is the cure for curiosity.

I once led a workshop for a group of school district administrators. These people, former teachers now mock gods, had no curiosity at all. They got paid to know and no they did. Don't let the "k" or the "w" fool you, know means no.

No talking, no sitting, no loitering, no swearing, no kissing, no loving, no yes. Who says? The problem with revolutions is that they are so messy? The other problem with them is that they always leave in place what they started with: get it? Revolution, something that goes round going round? Revolutions are too big; they are too general? Revolutions are what happens when too much has gone unflirted with? Revolutions are what happens when it is too late? Flirting is what happens when it is just a little

---

[7] Nope, the question marks aren't a mistake and I didn't get them on sale. They indicate, I hope, that you shouldn't trust anything that I say ever; you should always seek but not find your own revolution: resolution?

early, and seduction is what happens when it is perfectly on time?[7]

Please, please, please, please, please, practice. Practice the magical, the alchemic act of converting assertions, facts, to questions with curiosity. Remember it isn't fun to be in the castle under siege. You can't really learn about the castle while you are in it because you are too busy being in it. When you are outside the castle laying siege you can make the castle into anything; when you are in the castle it is too persistently what it is. It forces you into a defensive posture already fighting for what you think. Spiritual seduction is ceasing to be a person and laying siege on your personhood. Flirting is the step which returns you to an earlier intimacy with life on Earth. Intimacy is always more yes than no usually as the exception to the rule following elsewhere. This intimacy is necessary to reach outside yourself with sufficient confidence that the inside is taken care of while you are gone.

In the process of becoming engaged and entangled with spirituality you will have to be outside yourself a lot, getting things far and long that you don't think are part of you and bringing them back to integrate them. The simple trick in this chapter, when practiced a lot, frees you from the need to respond offering you a life as a stimulus, or at least not as a response and in the process making life sufficiently worth living that you can define yourself rather than having your circumstances define you. A very powerful trick indeed and one quite necessary for spirituality to lay siege to you.

A practice assault: "You look confused." Possible nondefenses: "What do I look like when I am confused?" or "What do you think I am confused about?" or "Do I look more or less attractive when I look confused?" or "Can you understand my confusion?"

There is typically one defense to an assault; there are always enough assaults to go a round and around.[8] If you don't respond to any assault you go around; if you do respond and defend you cease your movement. You stop and define yourself by something less than you are. The castle walls and moat are never far from where you stop. Defined as something less than you are you can't flirt and you are very far from seduction. You get stuck holding no. You get stuck defending something that you aren't even interested in. Isn't it the pits when the rightful owner of the castle you have been defending your whole life shows up to claim it? You are always defending something that *isn't* because *is* doesn't need any defense, making you at best redundant and tiresome.

Imagine that you have a sister two years your senior. You hate your sister. Mom always liked her better than she liked you, so did dad. As a child she stole both your friends and your thunder, making you afraid of thunder and the storm so necessary in a life lived largely. Mom decided that it was inconvenient to have two birthday parties a year so she just had one on your sister's birthday. They named you Judy Jr. after your sister Judy. You never got anything you wanted; she stole your man, she got better grades than you, she got better presents than you, she was smarter than you; the only thing she got less than you was beaten up and abused.

This whole time she refused to acknowledge the difference in the treatment you received as did everybody else. Finally, in your late fifties you met a man your sister couldn't steal. She got terminally ill and you had to forgo the man to try and save her.

---

[8] What if, upon getting to Heaven you find you have arrived where there isn't a gate? Would you go searching for a gate? Would you ask others about entry points? Some people won't even ask for directions here on Earth. Some people have to follow directions. Heaven is always closed at first, a little test to find out if you learned to flirt and seduce while on Earth. If you didn't you might get to use that gift certificate after all.

Over the thirty years of her "terminal illness" you did everything you could for her short of frying up your right arm and feeding it to her. She did get your kidney and your goat. After all, "what are sisters for?" When your mother died she left your sister everything. She even left a little piece of knowledge: your sister was adopted. Mom leaves everything to sis to make up for any discomfort (this fact finally disclosed) might cause her.

You pissed your life away for what? For something that you thought was true that wasn't? Anything that you think is true isn't; it just has you work for less than minimal wage to defend its truthfulness.

Enough already? Tap out!

You can stop pretending, tending before. The little trick of turning assertions into questions sets you free. Free of the need to respond. You will soon learn that freedom is the greatest burden that anyone can carry. Freedom is the key to unlimited responsibility; responsibility isn't anything like you thought it was. It is bigger, better, more useful and leads directly from flirting to seduction.

Please leave what you know behind and what you no. Leave it behind not because I asked you to or because of anything other than a whim. Better yet, leave it behind because you leave it behind.

CHAPTER 8

Degrees of Wonderful

We have to make life on Earth palatable. After all a man's gotta eat. Lately I have been breathing in Napoleon's air; apparently, given my height, things have been rising. Napoleon used to send a messenger letting his women know that he was only a week from home and they should not bathe. He wanted them to smell by the time he got home; that may just be a wives' tale. I would like to have been that messenger, though the risk would have been great, think of how nice they would have smelled. Napoleon just didn't know any better and he was the ruler of the known world. See I told you that knowing wasn't all it was cracked up to be.

Did you try the trick in the last chapter? Did it alter forever your relationship with boss, spouse, parents and friends? Yes, it really does work. This chapter contains another trick. When we got together last time we explored how to have the most fun by becoming the one laying siege to the castle rather than the one in the castle eating "C" rations and perpetually defending. Now it is time to discover just how much fun laying siege can be. It's a man's main line of offense against anything that looks excessively domestic. Once you have laid siege would you settle for anything else? Once you have tasted limelight nothing else will do. Community theater should precede the big time, not follow it.[1]

Laying siege is always more wonderful, not better, than not getting laid at all. As it is, is always better than defending: now let's explore the intriguing domain of the degrees of wonderful. *Hint:* Darwin didn't raise no babies or sissies; he wasn't that spiritual.[2]

You're going to have to stop the humanist within from whining, whatever it takes to do so. You're going to have to admit that at least,, to some degree, until you get comfortable here, there is going to be an element of competition in life and that, unlike a cruise ship, sometimes in life there is just not enough food to go around and that at other times in life there is a choice between your being the meal or somebody else and depending on who is doing the eating you might want to fight for the right for it to be you or the right for it not to be. So, and this is my real message here: Shut up when you want to make a point and talk when you have nothing to say. When you can do that people will want to listen and there is nothing much more rewarding than that other than getting to the point where you can pick both who listens and what they hear and this is the art of laying siege and making certain that siege and you are both well satisfied. This is impossible, but it will take practice.

We are leading up to the time for a cigarette. Three years ago my parents came to visit. I put them up in my room. We tried a wholetell first but they whined a lot and couldn't stand

---

[1] Some of you may still be upset with the reference to "man's" in the sentence above; some of you didn't even notice it; either way we have some work to do. If you are still upset over it and think it should have been "person's" then your medicine is to read the sentence again using "person's." See, feel and hear the difference. If you didn't notice it, I suggest that you invite in a little bit of the best of Gloria Steinem (that little bit of tenderness in her jaws and hairdo). Then notice that man's "really" does exclude the very women we wish to get lucky with.

[2] If you are going to be skittish you are going to be playing in a series of little relatively unconnected less than one act plays that will likely never have you in a big spotlight unless you buy it yourself and shine it on yourself which is always different than if someone else buys it and shines it on you.

the release of withholds or the time checking out. *Hint:* It never sounds good when your parents are whining because that always means that they want you to do something about it.[3] I slept elsewhere. It has taken three years to get the smell of my father's after-shave out of the room. I live in an expensive house, not the kind that you just get rid of a bedroom. Easier to rid myself of dad than his smell. I can offend him and he will leave but I am wondering what all he left behind in me that will sprout later. It wouldn't be worth finding out.[4]

I recently visited my parents and made the first sexual joke I have ever made with my father. He went to the pool to pay for my swim; what are fathers for? There was a pretty lifeguard there collecting money, of all things, for services not rendered. What are sons for? Remember: Sons will be fathers. He said, and you have to know that he has never said such a thing before, if this was one in a whole string of sausages it would not have been noteworthy but this was the first bite of meat for a vegan monk, the proverbial poon tang for the pope, or astro-not, though my father is no saint or I guess I wouldn't have been born, if you know what I mean. He said, "She wanted to go home with me."

The look of pride I saw on his face was well beyond anything I had ever seen there; it resembled what I see in the mirror when I have what it takes to look. It moved around from

---

[3] Almost nobody knows that in the process of creating fonts, there is a process called hinting. I have no idea what it is but I am not making it up. I suspect that in the process of becoming a real boy or girl there is also a process of hinting. I know more about this one; it has to do with telling you just what you don't want to hear when you don't want to hear it and it plays a perfectly integral part in interrupting your momentum getting to where you really didn't want to go anyway. I think hint is what they really meant when they said, "Saved by the bell."

[4] My father is my ultimate spell checker. This is neat, I call him with any word and he spells it quickly and accurately for me. I say, "Thanks, bye." He says, "Good-bye." I figure this little interchange is a tribute to Clint Eastwood, it goes ahead and makes our day.

cheek to lips finally settling in his eyes. I said, without a noticeable pause for his pending self-consciousness to undercut the moment, "I learned a long time ago that you don't take that kind home; you just do what you must do and shower when you get home."[5]

I have to risk breaking rapport here and tell you that, other than in print, I am and have always been a bit of a prude. That doesn't mean that I haven't done things that any good priest wouldn't try and keep quiet about. It does mean that given half a chance I will at least balk instead of crossing myself. Once crossed I figure the line could never be washed off. The difference between clean, relatively, sex and dirty sex is the number of lies told in the process. The difference between a clean, relatively, life and a dirty life is the number of lies told in the process. I, my pure self, had the same lifeguard thoughts as my dad, other than give her money. Had she asked I would have declined, so would dad, but since I thought she hinted I was more than willing to have this go somewhere in my head, the lusting in my heart beneath Jimmy Carter's belt. I had flirted with her at my first, and fastest rate but still wouldn't have seen our first kid together for at least 18 lifetimes. What are lifeguards for? A prophylactic against drowning in one's own tepid soup.[6]

If you are going to lay siege let's figure out the best way to do it. I have already let you know, about as specifically as I can, that you shouldn't bring your mom and dad along or anybody that you have to pay or who smells funny. You should

---

[5] Her name was Chlor Ine. Though my father wasn't familiar with her tricks,, I, having become a swimmer, was. I usually brought her home somewhat and always tried to get rid of her. She is one in a line of necessary evils and pleasures in my life. We have a kind of undeniable chemistry together.

[6] Not very often will I answer a question specifically but in this case it seemed too obvious. Sorry. Every once in a while I need to be acknowledged for my restraint, said the in mate. I could have said Intergalactic prophylactic against drowning in one's own tepid soup.

shower often between battles and enjoy your time away from the women. (That was the Napoleon part: Hindshadowing.)

RULES OF UNDERENGAGEMENT, UNENGAGEMENT AND ENGAGEMENT: HOW TO ENJOY THE SIEGE AS YOU ARE MAKING IT: PART A:

1) Never lead with an assertion, that lets them know where you are and who you are. Anybody not sufficiently confident of the ultimate outcome always leads with the facts as they know them and the facts "as they know them" are never facts at all just repeated fictions. In other words: Never go to the nonfiction part of the library if you are trying to discover how to live your life.[7]

2) Do you wonder what the second step is? Curiosity. You must lead with not knowing because then the person you are laying siege for will have to fill in the blank with something that they know, thus signing the reality check. Whoever pays the check pays the bill. You just have to not no what you are laying siege to. If you know what you are laying siege to you will always lose,, because even if you win you will get nothing bigger than your thinking, which if it was big enough already you wouldn't even be tempted to lay siege; you could just sit home and munch chips and watch *Andy of Mayberry* reruns and you certainly wouldn't have read this far in this book or even

---

[7] Many mornings ago, years, there was a knock at the door. It seems I had broken a rule. There was a wiry, bespectacled, mentally manacled man at my door. He wanted to know if I had thrown a bag of garbage in what seemed like, but apparently wasn't a public dumpster. He shook a very smudged looking letter at me with my address on it. Sherlock had found that letter in the bag and traced it, by the address, back to me. What was I to say? I said, "Do you work for the post office?" The I'm moral of this oratory is to be careful with your return address.

considered reading any of my other books which are listed boldly in the back of this one.

3) You have to not know what you are laying siege to so that when you win you will either be pleasantly surprised on the upside or pleasantly humored on the downside. Sometimes you will discover that what you won is an "all expense paid" shopping trip to Fort Knox while other times you will find out that you have won a can of peas. *Aside*: I have heard from a reliable source that due to the way canned vegetables come to market you are always eating last year's crops and that a kind of alchemy happens whereby the entire contents of the can turns from simple sugar, which is always quite tasty, to carbohydrates over the period of the year so not only doesn't what is in the can look like what went in but it also doesn't taste like it and it doesn't even give you any nutrition. I have the idea that canned humor is just this magical and nutritious. If you are going to lay siege you may as well be funny in the process.

4) You need to eat well when you are laying siege. You need to always eat well. If you are laying siege to get the cook or the really good food, then it is a siege with a purpose. The purpose always wears out in the process and if you visualize the end of the siege during the siege you will have missed the process and must now defend that end as the right and truly correct end.

5) There are many possible ends; the more ends you can have the easier it is to untangle this gnarled rope we call life. Have you ever been untangling a rope that only had two ends? It isn't easy and it gets progressively harder the longer the rope. Life gets progressively harder the longer it gets if there are not ends all along the way. Part of the lack of logic here is that if there is an end there is a beginning. There may be one end in life without a beginning: death maybe, but we will get to that later, death. All other ends in life have a beginning that follows

shortly after them and a neat little nap nestled between the two. My sister told me that a professor of hers once told her that the purpose of math is to let people know when to stop. We are a nation of math cripples and if you ever want anything of value to change, it had better be that first.[8]

6) Learn math. There is no aspect of math that doesn't lend itself to the successful enjoyment of the process of siege. Addition is obvious, subtraction two, geometry lets you know where you stand, algebra lets you question that, calculus keeps you busy, trigonometry lets you know where you don't stand and higher math is the door to spiritual ascension.

7) If you are going to have a great siege you need to know when it is over, like opera. There are two ways to know when it is over, you can look at the circumstances logically and rationally, keeping statistics and measuring all kinds of things: Have you read my new book, *Accountants at War?* Or you could trust yourself to declare the end, as you declared war in the first place.

8) The beginning has two possible courses. You can begin the siege when you are forced to, reacting to something or other, like the U.S. goes to war, or, you can wait until you have nothing at all to react to and begin any new siege you want with any cute or handsome person you wish. There is good evidence, in my head, that couples of arranged marriages do better than couples who are allowed to pick their own spouses. If that doesn't tell you something about free choice you don't have any choice about thinking that choice is worth having.

9) Any lie is always indicative of an underlying no. Every lie you tell while you are on a siege puts you at least one step closer to being the one under siege. If you lie about how tall the

[8] They put the math handicapped spaces close to the mall because the people who park there overspend living on credit, as close to immortality as most of them will get, this not paying your bills from this month until next month. Economics and mathematics are branches of philosophy.

walls are, you will either have too hard a time climbing them or too easy a time. Either way you will distrust yourself. Studies have been done that indicate that how tired a person is alters their perception of the percentage grade of a slope they are asked to climb. Wearing a heavy backpack also alters the perception of the slope in an upward direction. Do the math Lie + Lie + Lie + Lie equals Spin. Spin is movement around rather than movement toward. The more you spin the more you miss the little irregularities of life that are put there to increase your attention and make life interesting. You wouldn't go out in the battlefield and spin around in plain sight for everybody to see and if you did that it wouldn't matter how smart you thought you were or how invisible. It is not an accident that a dog spins in circles at two points in her life. She spins when she is chasing her tail, not getting anywhere, and she spins right before she drops her bag of bones down to sleep. It is not an accident that all politicians care about is spin and nobody cares about them. You have to learn to move forward, ever-forward without spin, that is the nature of a siege with your context changing as you advance with you not on greased wheels but in shoes that fit just right so that no matter what you are advancing into, you look forward like Cinderella, not too much but just the right amount, to the next step.[9]

10) You have to be smart, very smart, smart enough to complete the circle on its own without adding anything, so smart that you don't trust your own intelligence. There is a certain level of intelligence that trusts itself, just one pinch smarter, intelligence that remains and doesn't respond in a pinch, and you have the intelligence, the natural intelligence to enjoy your lack of understanding of your context—circumstance.

---

[9] One shoe is better than two only in fairy tales and you should never put your best foot first because then you have nothing to look forward to.

11) If things are changing faster than you are changing you are at least under the threat of threat. If things are changing more slowly than you are things are a bore. You have to maintain the pace of the siege so that just nothing remains the same creating overlying contexts sufficient to erase all lies. Wouldn't it be neat if two lies created a truth because then all you would need is to make certain that you were stuck to even numbers?

12) For the enjoyment of a siege you must have an appreciation for the appetite of each cell, have a measurement of its specific permeability, its past permeability and an extrapolation of where permeability is going. Any siege happens on many levels and the permeability of each cell within you is always the best indication of an interim victory or an ultimate defeat.[10]

13) Life will always be better during the siege than it is after. During the siege you are closer to process than when you are under siege. You are always laying siege or under siege: there is no siegeless time, thus life is always better.

Here are some examples where you can apply the above thirteen rules, for those of you who are not clear, of, on, what a siege is. A siege is the allies in World War II, it is you trying to convince your spouse to take the garbage out, it is your seeking a raise or new job, it is you trying to have sex with someone willing or not, it is you trying to grow, it is you trying to rid your lawn of weeds once and for all, it is going home for Christmas or deciding this year not to go home, it is checking out a library book and checking out anything you perceive not to be yourself. These are all examples of sieges that you might lay. Sieges that might be laid on you include the Germans in World War II, your spouse trying to convince you to take the garbage out, somebody seeking a raise or job from you, somebody trying to

---

[10] Permeability is always the measure of a successful siege. The more permeable your cells are the better the siege.

have sex with you, somebody trying to have you grow, the weeds trying to take over YOUR lawn, a Christmas play needing to be expressed; it is the book wanting to stay with its pals on the library shelf, that friction you get when you slide it away from the other books on either side and slide its weight off the shelf onto your arm.

So many sieges, so much to practice; so much play, so much to notice. Any bit of ground you gain on one siege counts in all others but is always less perceptible in the others. Ground gained in one is ninety eight percent metaphorical in another but two percent real and that two percent is available through optional input as to the direction your life is going. Apply the above rules to your sieges a little at a time and you will discover the delightful bittersweet flavor that being present during a siege gives as it whittles away at the end-not-being-relevant, with a parade to celebrate the process.

Do you know how many people quickly go down'hill and die after they retire? Studies indicate that it is a lot. If quitting work can have this effect think of how terrible the repercussions are to quitting play. We call the repercussions of quitting play work. It is time to play; every siege should be play and the main way it stays that way is moving from optional to mandatory while your little feats remain in place.

CHAPTER 9

Flirting With Seduction

That is enough playing tag with the catatonics. If we can convince you that you cannot have everything you want, it isn't long until you learn that you can't appear or disappear anything anytime which makes you the potential victim of something we already have in inventory. Do you know how many silk stockings the troops purchased during the war? Do you know how many they wore? *Hint:* The number they bought is a lot and the number they wore is a multiple of zero. There is nothing like a war to get your hopes up. A war is a lot of "this" place "isn't it," "this" time "isn't now," and "things will get better" kind of thing.[1]

Multiple sieges add up to a war. Multiple seizures add up to a victory and endless de feats add up to defeat. Do the math: if you play you can't win because winning is the absence of play. If you continue to play you haven't yet won and you haven't yet lost which is the place of greatest attention. You can't not play because by the time you get there the play has already begun. You can ignore the play but only at the peril of your senses and humors.

I had no where to get with the cute little blonde, but to keep my attention there and continue to play I needed to keep playing.

---

[1] I will let off when the status quo is an orphan. A lonely only child too set in its ways to be adopted by anyone, two or three.

Three months later we got together again and things had advanced in my absence.[2]

She got ever more willing though not yet up to the level of participating actively. She could kiss. Oh my gosh we almost wore our lips out: she said "no" with those same lips. By morning after morning I could hardly speak. We kissed for hours; we exercised our tongues. I was in Heaven. Kissing led to exploring her chest, which naturally, with another three-month absence and a return from other wars led to moving farther south. There should be some sort of "warning" label on a bomb. Everything that you do is worth a certain amount of time. If it took you three years to plan the trip to the end of the driveway to get the mail and another two to execute it, there better be something other than Christmas catalogs and electric bills when you get there. It is never too soon to receive your inheritance. Anything I did down south just wasn't worth it. I tried CPR, tenderness, roughness, negotiation. I tried everything I knew but assuming participation, I imagined participation but didn't assume it. In other words, the one thing that I wasn't willing to do is go on without her awake, alert and overtly willing. It would have had to have been another virgin birth.

---

[2] You don't ever learn things while you are learning them. You learn them when you have been exposed to them and then taken a break from them. A kid learns to ride a bike by trying and then taking time away from trying. While away the mind does the necessary dry runs without the threat of bike to integrate what isn't, a rider, with what is, falling down. In the presence of the threat of falling down, the rider is nowhere to be found. Wouldn't it be neat if the school system learned this? I guess for them to learn it we would have to have the school system fail at their primary task, indoctrination under the guise of teaching, then close down for a while so that each lieutenant in the classroom could get sufficient perspective to discover that in the game of life they do more falling down than riding and that in order to teach riding it really would be better if they learned how to ride what they don't yet know how to ride rather than doting on what they do.

This was fun. It was exciting. It smelled like a French bakery, but at a certain point it just wasn't worth going on. At this point one random ulterior motive is enough to ruin a lifetime. Some people would have married her, others would have gone ahead without the mandatory eight count, still others would have stopped and been willing to live with the frustration, some would have gotten mad and gotten gone. You have to know when to quit flirting. You have to know when what you are after is no longer worth the time or effort. The sooner you can access this end, the safer you will be. Learning with the least effort is the key and going past this point would have required more effort than learning. She wanted to teach me the same thing over and over while learning nothing herself. Even French pastry isn't worth that. Learning is my Waterloo.

If you are picking apples and you have a lot of apple trees you may want to pick the apples that are within reach on many of the trees before you spend too much time risking life and limb trying to pick the ones that are hard to reach. If you have to get all the apples from one tree before you can move on to another you really aren't a very good student of economics or romance are you?

You need to know when to quit and the time to quit is when you don't want to—when things are working. It would be a much less interesting world if people acted in their own best interest. Typically they don't and if invited to would rather go to war defending what they don't want, don't need and can't stand. They fight too often for the exceptions while following the rules that they really should be fighting. If you get on somebody's side you will soon discover that you are alone. I know this has happened to you but you may not have noticed it because it is just too ridiculous to have happened.

You will have things that you don't get done in this lifetime. You will also have things that you do get done. If you dwell more on one of these than the other that dwelling indicates what stage of life you are in. If you dwell more than fifty percent on the things that you have done you are too old to create something; if you dwell more than seventy-five percent on the things you haven't done you are reaching the end. If you focus on what you are doing you are immortal. None of this has to do with chronology. I never did have sex with her. It is one of my few happy regrets. I did learn more with her than sex could have possibly taught me. Don't ever have sex with someone you don't want to be the parent of your child. You deserve better than that. In fact: as a man one part of me wishes that you would never have sex with anyone again. Another part wants to benefit from the experience of others and urges you on. Which one rules the day depends almost entirely on whether I perceive that you are on my team or not. If you are on my team I want the best for you and if you are not I want the least for you. In my best moments everybody is on my team; in my worst moments only one person is; in my spiritual moments there is no team: just all.

Somebody else had sex with that little blonde, several somebody elses and they fit into one of two categories: Those who knew enough to regret it. And those who didn't.

You have to flirt everywhere because flirting is the way you find out about the terrain.

We recently bought the piece of property next to our house. It is nine acres of oak woods. Our other property is primarily hilly pasture. The pasture, at one level, takes very little to explore, you look at it, "yes, there it is." The oak woods can't be explored so easily. At a much deeper level, looking at tiny things, the pasture and oaks could each take a lifetime to get to know. The smaller things you can perceive and celebrate the more attention and celebration you will have. With her, I celebrated each step, the ones taken and the ones not. She learned,

I learned and there is no end to flirting, only an expansion of what one can flirt with. Flirting makes your world bigger. As it gets bigger it just gets too big for one. You must either hire somebody to take care of part of your world or love somebody to do so. In the case of an employee they will leave most of their own world behind and for a specific fee take care of part of yours: mercenary. In the case of love they will, in return for everything, do just the parts they want to do always trying to negotiate upward. And that is if you got a good one. Bad ones just sort of lie there lying, wanting nothing more for you or them. The good ones want all of your attention and continually add more needs to be taken care of than you could ever have imagined: alien. Thus they stretch your imagination and your attention. You love to complain as they do this and life isn't so sweet without it.[3] You just aren't ready for love until you can flirt with anyone, anytime, shamelessly. Your world needs to be big enough to bring another person into it. You need to be able to flirt all the time because being in love is a full-time job flirting.

The nature of love is inclusion. The process of love is continually roving the alleged border between the two or more of you and breaking down anything that gets in the way of the two of you being one. Old insecurities get in the way, new insecurities crop up too, doing anything gets in the way, knowing anything blocks the flow between the two of you almost entirely. Going to work separates you without lifting, talking to anyone else gets in the way, often talking to each other gets in the way even more, having sex can get in the way

---

[3] Everybody wants control without responsibility. These two don't go together but they can't be separated either because control doesn't exist and responsibility does. You can't separate something that does exist from something that doesn't because they are already under the deepest influence of difference that they can be. If you pretend that they are the same, you miss just about everything.

and not having sex definitely gets in the way. There are two groups of effectors to this new and budding relationship that you have earned by flirting: there are the things that obviously get in the way and those that not so obviously get in the way. If you respond there is implication in that response that there is something outside yourself. If it is outside yourself then it is something that you will interact with at a more superficial level than love.

Flirting is an immature relationship but fundamental to learning about relating. Flirting is laying siege and being able to quit. A more mature relationship excludes only the option to quit. I called it quits with the blonde because I could, because it wasn't that much fun anymore, because we weren't getting anywhere, because I learned what I needed to from her, because she wasn't even the shadow of the one, because I basically didn't even like her, because she was crazy and committed to remaining a certain kind of crazy that didn't really interest me. Because she wanted to tell me the same thing over and over again and it was always about things that weren't really true and always about her. I can still think about her and smile; I can still think, should I have a little spare time or have a cold, that we might still fool around but I got on with life. She, and this is a real indication that it was time to quit, didn't. She is the same; I am fundamentally different.[4]

---

[4] If you are, and you are, fundamentally a nestling, then you have a difficult job in the face of danger. You have to look out for yourself and your species in various orders. Her order was always the same; she would not take care of herself first and then not take care of her species. She would not take care of herself consciously and not take care of her species unconsciously. This isn't really something I wanted passed on to the next generation. Isn't it odd that the only test for being a good parent comes in the form of the child as the tester? If they aren't a good lover they won't be a good parent and if they are a good lover there are other hoops to fry.

Spiritual Seduction

When you have flirted a lot, when you can reach out to anyone and find the no's without being scared of them, then you are ready for a much deeper relationship. You are ready to move into the castle and figure out how to get along with the resident there as you become the resident there. The siege is over not by having won or lost, but by growing out of it and into a much fuller exchange than battle. The nature of battle is that the exchange is limited, so limited. Battle is a very immature expression of connection. Competition of all kinds should be limited to those who don't know themselves; and it is. The idea is to apply force where there is weakness so that force overcomes the weakness. In the next level of relating the idea is to apply force in the greatest area of force and weakness in the greatest area of weakness which has the vibration of two become the vibration of one, a kind of sympathetic joining without any sympathy.

Hint: Never take your clothes off around someone unless you are very comfortable with them with your clothes on. Never go to bed with someone you wouldn't want to go clothes shopping with.

On the road to seduction you must first confront a lot of no's and learn to deal with them. It is much easier to deal with the no's of others than it is with your own. It is often hard to even see that you have any, you the perfect one, you the unexamined one, you the one who never arrives with more no's than yeses loaded, you who have never learned that it is easier to say no than to think: oh, yes you. The nature of a no is that it looks permanent and non-negotiable. Through flirting you can discover what is negotiable and what is not. Everything is negotiable: until you know that everything is negotiable your playground has fences and walls and anything lying outside them is no longer playground. When you can be nourished by a constant diet of no's you are ready for a deeper relationship and ready for the task at hand, converting no to yes.

74

Anyone who has amateur parents has a lot of impacted no's. Anyone who grew up in a world with other people has a lot of lingering and latent no's. Anyone with a name is defended by the need to assert power by saying no. Saying no seems to be a more fundamental right than saying yes. We defend with no; we attack with yes. It is always more fun to attack life than it is to defend it.

I found the cute blonde's no. A no that wasn't worth the negotiation. A no that she wanted to hold in place more than she wanted a white picket fence, a Moon Pie, a good time or verification that she was loved. A looming, daunting, haunting, persistent, terrible no. It could have been negotiated but most mediation, discussion or pretense of openness is about time. Clockwise is not as wise as indicated because it rules out Skinner by preempting the possibility of eternity, making some shorter period seem more important thus pre-emptying eternity—the legitimate mother of all rewards. It would have taken too much time to convert her, a conversion is worth only a point or two, and the more time I spent with her the longer time seemed. In deep enough pain, time turns into eternity, just the other side of the present moment. It would take more time than I wanted to invest, and obviously, by the fact that she is still alone and I am still together with more people than ever, others considered her not worth the lack of risk and her stifling predictability inspiration to seek treasure elsewhere. She is still cute; the mirror tells her so when she is able to listen.[5]

Hint: If your collection of ex-wives or ex-husbands would or do like each other then you have not grown or learned enough from these relationships. You need to get going, get learning and find someone that your patterns don't pick. In other words:

---

[5] Cuteness is not a long-term hold. It is something that you hold in your portfolio for a very short time and then trade up to smart, interesting or pretty. As a long-term hold it withers and wrinkles.

Marry someone that you can't stand now so that you can love them later, rather than someone that you love now who you won't be able to stand later.

Victories with little no's, converting them to ambivalence or yes, prepares you for breaking down the boundaries between yourself and another. Being able to convert any no to yes and being in the presence of another who can do the same has you be ready for spirituality. When you can face the no that someone worships more than anything else in the world, only a spiritual path leads around it. Worshiping no is worshiping limitation. Yes, almost every religion on the planet is based on no. Yes, almost every relationship is based on no. Yes, the Ten Commandments are stated in the negative.

Hint: You must play with what you wouldn't do deeply enough until you discover the amazing differences between what you wouldn't do and what you couldn't do. Then you must expand what you can't do converting the can'ts to cans. Equipped with enough cans you can share them with others less well-endowed. When you have had enough of the inherent superiority in such a relationship you can share your cans with those with more cans, you can then take the humor always inspired by such a situation and spread it everywhere.

Let me make this more obvious. If you don't have any money you need to get some money. Then you need to spend the money so that you don't have any money. Then you need to get more money than you can spend. Then you need to give money to those less able or flush than you. Once you have helped enough of those people, and they hate you enough, you must give money to people who don't need it. Giving money to people who don't need it is funny and it moves you up the scale to where your currency is no longer money but funny. You must then find things funny. Then you must find things funny that you have never been able to find funny before. Then you must learn to have other people find things funny. Then you have to have people who already find things funny find things even funnier and then you get kicked, softly, upstairs to pure attention. Then you must run through the entire cycle again with pure attention. Pure attention means attention without the bias of humor.

The more you can play in the process and progress, the more inspired you will be to progress.

This openness is scary. If you live fully enough death becomes erotic. Hold my hand would ya?

CHAPTER 10

Having, Halfing & Holographs

I am reminded of Tchaikovsky's Sixth Symphony, *Pathétique*, and tempted to add a fifth movement based on the melody of *Don't Worry Be Happy*. That or the great homosexual Ninth Symphony of Beethoven, *The Ode to Boy*.

In other words: You can have a relationship until you die but you can't really live without one. Anything you do before you die is risking your life. While it is useful and often expansive to risk your life it is hard to stay present in the process. You need to learn to be present at the threat of death opening up the possibility of discovering that you really aren't threatened with death more than several times a second. Every no is a metaphor for death, every yes a metaphor for life. The transition from head to heart requires the death of anything that one perceives oneself to be. Not the temporary death of a nap or cruise control, but a factual death in fact.

You can't live fully or anything resembling fully until you aren't even sure that you can't know anything for sure. You live in a world of facts. These facts keep you from other people. If their facts are your facts it looks as though you are connected, if their facts aren't your facts it looks as though you aren't even related.

You need to move from dishonest nonmonogamous relationships to dishonest monogamous relationships, then to honest monogamous relationships then to honest nonmonogamous relationships. The trick here is that you need to begin lying to many people, rather than claiming that you are telling the truth, and slowly work your way to lying to fewer, then tell the truth slowly to one person playing your way up to telling the truth to many people.[1] The purpose of relationship is to disseminate the truth, creating a condition of evangelical trust in nothing in particular other than the process of spreading the truth. Each time the truth alters, and it should alter often, people are invited to get off, escape, with what they have won so far or continue on the journey.

A person's rules and the truth do not overlap, they are mutually exclusive, even hating each other. If the truth is hard to tell it is only because it either isn't the truth anymore or never was. If a rule is followed nothing is learned.

Let's take a rule as an example: "You should share." Most of you were taught that at an early age. Well, at least somebody tried to share that rule with you. At the time you were trying your best to learn it, you still remembered that "share" was a metaphor for "loss" because what it really means is that you can't have the whole thing. The undermining presupposition here in the whole idea of sharing is that there isn't enough to go around. The truth that is missed here is that having is wholographic. No matter how small a piece you have, you have

---

[1] There is just no way around tracing the sine, rollercoaster, wave. That is, other than getting to the point of sufficient dispersal which is only possible when you have escaped dichotomy entirely. This magical point is called love if it is from the outside in and explosion if it is from the inside out, so one fundamental step to getting there is knowing what is inside you and what is outside you. While this is easy to say I invite you to notice that reading me saying it is from the outside and it loses something, being nicked by your no's, on the way in. When a perfect translation between in and out happens you will broaden your definition of sex and always be having it. Not bad, or good either.

the whole thing.[2] Rationally, there is a thin line between having and not having that is drawn by lining ducks up, and ducking up not down, to be counted, by something seemingly outside yourself. The relevant line of having is drawn within you. You can define having in so many different ways; you have had experiences of this but haven't really noticed them. You have had a pen in your hand and really had the pen. You have left the pen at home when you went to work, but still you have the pen. You have lost a pen, thought you didn't have it anymore and then found it under your dresser a year later. *Aside*: The moral here is that you should clean under your dresser more often.

You have had a pen, given it to somebody else and had even a greater experience of having it when they had it, not just because they may take better care of it than you but also because you want them to have some part of you which the pen is a metaphor phor. You have found a pen and experienced a time period between finding it and when it becomes something of yours; this period of time is called the windfall quotient. I once knew a man that was struck on the head and killed by a windfall; my father, who art in Wisconsin, composed a song about it called: *Lucky Hymn*.[3]

You have seen a pen that you wanted, not bought it and wished you had. You may even have seen a pen that someone else had and wished that it was yours but didn't ask for it without

---

[2] You have the whole thing because it is representative. The best you will do in this lifetime is have a sample of something and generalize to the whole. Since that is the best you can do we may as well, wherever useful, pretend that the sample is the whole knowing that it is not.

[3] I have considered the idea of legal money laundering. It works like this: You get five percent of a person's inheritance for handling the 83 million dollars for the person in such a way, spaced over time, so that they perceive that they have earned the money. Windfalls are easily lost or squandered; work ethic demands that money earned is money owned. This business would really work; all that I ask is you set it up yourself and get rich and that you call it *Wings Inherited Laundering Bizarre*.

ever really exploring the wholographic nature of having. You have had a pen you didn't care about. You have had a pen stop writing just when you needed it to write and considered the possibility that if there were a God she wouldn't let this happen; or maybe the pen, and everything else, is really against you. You have not had a pen when you needed to write something down. You have marveled at the whole idea of a pen: so much meaning pouring from such a tiny Whole. You have, I hope, shared a pen with a friend sending a letter and pen to the friend and them sending back a reply and another pen for you to write it with. You have been lying down trying to write with a pen and had gravity fight your next word by having the angle of the pen against you.

I could go on, but I think you get the idea. If the idea you got is that pens are versatile and valuable writing tools then you missed the point. If you got the idea that you could corner the market on pens just by broadening your definition of ownership, you went a little farther with me but still left the rose before it bloomed. If you, and this is 84 percent of you, realized that the pen is a metaphor for anything including relationship and that you have to progress beyond a geographically impaired model of relating all the way to one which goes from the smallest, youngest possible moment to eternity and that you have never met anything that isn't yours, always, then you not only got the point but own the point. You have it, and like all having, it is in spite of yourself.

I was looking at a piece of property to buy. It contained half of a lake and about three hundred acres: think big. The real estate man, a friend, in a weak moment, looked at me and said, "Imagine people thinking they can really own land." It was later that he told me the price for not owning this particular piece. The lack of a sheepish look on his face indicated that he had forgotten his moment of clarity.

Spiritual Seduction

Sixteen years ago there was a knock on the door of my apartment in Whitefish Bay (White Folks Bay), Wisconsin. It was my friend Ed. Ed smoked three packs of cigarettes a day but each day created his lungs as pink and clean, sort of a mind over idiocy thing, which is a race that even the winner loses. Ed was to marry in two weeks. Luckily he had found his bride already; I was to be his best man. I have never understood why somebody getting married should need a best man. The idea of picking what is assumably the best woman, to marry, and the best man all within a short period of time has always seemed too difficult to me. This was exactly Ed's problem: He had picked the best man and the wrong woman. She wasn't really the wrong woman, just the wrong woman for him. She bought him cigarettes and had lived with him coughingly for fifteen years. It seemed to me that she didn't have his best interest at heart or anywhere else. It also seemed to me that she didn't have, nor was she interested in developing, the ability to sell Ed the most useful things a couple can share. In other words: They were going to legitimatize a kind of lazy death pact in which the pair would be substantially less than the sum of their parts. Statistically and from a marketing perspective this made no sense to me ever and for a brief moment it made no sense to Ed. In a clear moment we might call a revelation, Ed realized he was making a mistake, sort of a beggar's remorse. He not only didn't want to marry her, but he didn't even like her. Culture's words for this are "cold feet," which means that he saw something real in a sea of pus. This lasted about four hours. I fed it some leftovers and declined to let it smoke in my house. It left, the wedding went on and I discovered that Ed had a cousin who was nineteen, quite thin, mysterious (as are all the ones you don't know), sexy and this is the best part, interested in me. There was a part of Ed that died that day. He could have his remorse quickly before the wedding; after it the remorse came so slowly that it just ran his life from the background.

If you acted in your own best interest what you want when

gotten would make you happy. The solution for this little twist of faith is to want everything and never share anything. Give completely each moment as though it might not be your last. Follow the progression of relating outlined earlier, subscribe to my new journal, *The Changing Truth*, it comes out each second and all you have to do is be totally peaceful, not talking even to yourself in your own head and you will hear it. If you hear it occasionally you will call it intuition. If you hear it more often you will call it a wonderful life. *Aside*: It isn't really my journal, it is broadcast by the universe always. The universe is so polite that it won't interrupt anything you think, do, or identify with to give you the time accurately. Have you ever noticed that the Swiss can make a great watch but can't tell when it is time to get on somebody's side?

Cliff's Notes – Chapter 10: Relationship is always worth having. If you are growing you will have different and ever-better qualities of relating if you mature. The essence of having a relationship is realizing that any having is all having and knowing in the souls of your feet that you can't possibly lose anything. You can temporarily forget where you put it, but as long as it is still somewhere it is still yours. You could also have picked up from this chapter that the smaller you think you are the bigger will be your problems relatively. There are some more things you could have learned but I don't remember them right now so you may want to go back and read this chapter again especially if you have told more than two lies in the past year. A lie is not an inaccuracy, it is an intentional inaccuracy. It is deferring to the mind instead of the mouth. It is putting how you look ahead of how you live. Relationship is your salvation and you must be successful at relationship before you can begin exploring spirituality. You better get going because relationship must be taken care of by the time you are forty or you will be penalized three enjoyment points and two hunch points a week until you have taken care of it.

CHAPTER 11

Relating: The Beginning of Seduction or Hell

You need to find someone with a very different shoe size than yours. This is important for several reasons, none of them spiritual but all of them leading there if you know the path and if you can find some way to have the other person's shoes fit so that you won't have to walk in, on, your own.

Relating with somebody on Earth is easier, much easier than wearing their real teeth. It is harder than wearing or inspiring their smile when they don't want to give it. The marriage vows capture it when they say for worse or for worser. I am trying to start with the bad stuff leading to the good stuff later, and isn't that enough to ruin a possibly wonderful chance at post-marital intimacy?

I was leading a two-week course when my tooth started to really hurt. Two days of such pain and I discovered what an endodontist is. He takes something that hurts already and puts an ice stick on it to have it hurt more so that he can drill a hole in something that should be left in tact so that it can die and remain in your mouth and all this only costs about forty-five minutes and seven hundred dollars. And my point is: You just want to have someone there holding your hand or at least there

84

other than the endodontist; someone who cares while you are going through such things. If you think you want somebody there in those tough moments you are going to pee in your pants when you have somebody there when you have too much ecstasy to carry and the elevator doors are closing and you are in a hurry to get home into bed, not alone, and they sweep up some of your ecstasy mix it with theirs until it is indistinguishably both of yours and you realize that it is, after all, possible to like your own reflection in the deeper depths of another: love.

Can I tell you a secret? The endodontist may not love you but the tooth fairy does. Do you know why? Because you have teeth.

You get to love them with or without teeth. You get to love them when they are saying yes and when they are saying no. Any preference for anything from them is an attempt to shape their behavior to some other behavior that will contribute to your not growing. Until you can make them perfect you can't be. It is the looking in their eyes and seeing your reflection that may startle you especially if it looks like you are really in there. Remember the dog with a big bone in his mouth who looks into the pond and can't believe his luck? He opens his mouth to get that other bone because, at least in a dog's world holding one just isn't the same as seeing one. Of course the bone drops into the water and is gone, leaving two dogs and no bones, but ripples all around. Both dogs smile, just a little, revealing that there will be no jealously if there is no bone. Dogs just aren't that mature. Did I tell you that I love you? I do. I don't love everybody who reads these words: I love you. Spirituality is like that, human love is not. Oddly, spirituality allows specific love in a general case while humanness seldom allows love at all but if it does it is always general love in a specific case. Otherwise you wouldn't need to have so many cars to pick from in the lot when you go car shopping. You pick such a small percentage of what is there and then wonder why you aren't really happy with what you picked.

I once knew a man who was a chauffeur for a rich woman's cat. They, the man and the cat, conspired together. He took the cat where it wanted to go even when the owner indicated some other direction. You think that you would like it if people did what you said; you wouldn't, and the best place to find that out too late is in a closer personal relationship: always closer.

So there are two of you sitting by the fire. One wants to go up to bed and the other one does not. Neither wants to be alone, both are. There are two preferences living side by side with the only warmth available in the room coming from the fire. It just isn't how it should be.

I think that a first date should go on for two weeks. It should include the best sex you two have ever had together and neither one of you should buy dinner. Preferably nobody else should be around other than to provide nearly invisible services that you need, like making the bed over and over and having just the right food show up at just the right time. A first date should start out better than anything you have ever imagined and rise from there. You haven't settled for anything less have you? You can't settle for anything less in marriage or you will start blaming the other person for what doesn't work. Most people get married because they can't stand themselves anymore. There is nothing like a marriage to cast a loving light on your singlehood.

Hell is marrying her because she has a socket wrench that you need for a specific job, while later finding out that she borrowed the wrench from an old friend of hers who is leaving town, taking said wrench with her. Hell is marrying him when he is one age and then having him change ages without telling or consulting you.

Heaven is spending all of your time with somebody who is better each second than you ever imagined possible because you are growing.

It will happen, they will say no and you will want to strangle them, or they will say yes and you will wish they hadn't.[1] There are many false layers that make up a human being. There are layers that say yes and layers that say no. There are layers that you will like and ones that you will hate. You can cook up the whole onion or you can cook up only the odd or even layers. If you cook up only the odd ones you will waste the even ones and have to keep careful count. Very few people know that the odd layers of an onion taste very different than do the even ones. Not everything that lots of people think is true is true and not everything that nobody thinks isn't true isn't but the onion one is definitely a fabrication of mine as far as I can tell, and what I am telling you is that the best you can do is survive and subsist if you have any preference for one of their layers over another. You have to embrace all of them, not all at once but one little bit at a time pretty quickly.

Earth has a north pole and a south pole. These two are about as far apart as they can get and you wouldn't want to live in either for long.[2] On Earth, with immaturity, you will be pulled by two extremes. You will tithe to the illusion of division simply by putting toast in your toaster or arguing with a loved one or driving both to and from work. You will be caught out of reach of your loved one by nonexistent, invisible, but loud.

---

[1] They will say no to you proving that you can't have your way or they will say yes to something or somebody that you can't say yes to, again pointing out your limitation when all you want is to be held that moment. Sack races are less fun if you think you are going somewhere specific and need to be on time: see relationship.

[2] Sometimes it is really useful to remember that lease is as close to life as you can get and that you are just visiting and that company often gets special treatment even in the meanest householding.

The whole idea of the truth shouldn't even appear in life until thirty years of age. I mean, the idea can show up but some ideas are so tempting.[3] The idea of the truth means that you can have God on your side, thus always win and never be little, "wrong runs out the door, and takes play with it," because play, early play, always happens between poles. There should be an *Introduction to the Truth* course for all thirty-year-olds. In this course flexibility will be taught, because if there is anything that must go along in equal doses with the truth, it is the broadest range of motion possible.[4] The two or three of you are never dealing with the truth; you are a clash and sometimes an embrace of personal models becoming more impersonal by their blending. Each movement you make toward more impersonal, if unilateral, is met with resistance as the ways that one has misidentified oneself usually don't volunteer for those dangerous spy missions into the depths of another.[5] As late as possible creativity in relationship should be rewarded because truth tends to put out the fire of creativity. In early stages it is easy because the stage decorations aren't set and must be created. But later, when everything is set it gets to be razed and begun again without even Polaroids of the original to dominate by

---

[3] Yes, I am saying that your first day of Sunday school should happen about thirty years after your first day of regular school which shouldn't happen at all (see John Taylor Gatto or call for one of his tapes).

[4] The *Truth* course would be a little like hunter's safety. Hunter's safety is offered, I think, because guns are not really that safe. The truth has killed way more people and continues to than guns could. Maybe we need to start an organization called NTA, National Truth Association, National Truth Ass for short. To get into the NTA you would have to prove sufficient phlexability to carve your way out of several mental and physical traps in the face of public outcry. The mark of an NTA member is that they would show more than they say, being high class models that you would love to wake up with in the morning because they look just as good when you are making up as when you were breaking up.

[5] See Stocking's *Degrees of Abandonment Theory*.

Xeroxing. A new and deeper creativity can show up later in life, one based on accessing the truth, but this preempts the possibility of being wrong or right, and screams for both of you to go together, giving each other a hand up, not out. At a certain point you just must get close enough to somebody to stand on your own next to someone who is. You need to play in the polar world until you can tolerate both poles easily, then the truth can show up and show you who you really are in the face of all the false yous that you have created. Illusion should dominate the first third of life because it is only in illusion that you can make up anything you want in reaction or out of reaction to how things really are without concern for how they are. Early on you are better off buying and selling illusion than getting down to the process of knitting your own knitty gritty: knotty gritty. You know, no, because it is just too threatening to yes.

With the pair of you overlapping in illusion, there are bound to be messes. Your reason says that your survival is threatened so you must reproduce: children, thoughts, breakfast, anything. It is a very thin reason and proves itself to be such overtime. The degree to which you support each other in illusion is the degree to which you don't contribute to the other's best interest.

It would be tragic if it wasn't so consistent: you meet the truth, forget its face and name and go on with illusion in the name of truth. You only get blamed for this if your truths are different, may they always be different. This façade dooms a couple to personal life. Façade does that. It dooms the second and third thirds of life to defense, defense of what isn't in the face of the offer of what is. This is the main reason that people's lives often don't seem to be offering exactly what they had hoped for: in the face of them offering less and less they get offered less and less: there will be balance.

How will I know when this book is successful? First and least is that when I finish it, this wound that is bleeding profusely onto the page will never heal and second and more importantly the words that I have made up in this book, the ones that when you read them you know they aren't words, but they make sense, because I really have made them up, show up in the dictionary. You need to rise to ever greater tests really just testing your maturity.

It is at the border of truth and illusion that you must have somebody other than yourself around. I remember many years ago I did some cocaine, just for a short time and not really much. Cocaine had me think that everything was perfect. I started with a tiny bit and worked my way down to nothing as I learned to produce the same state in myself without the confection. I have had a harder time doing this with ice cream and elephants' ears, which in my opinion should be illegal along with "bad" cheese. When I thought everything was perfect, on cocaine, it wasn't. I found this out by playing ping-pong. I thought I was the best ping-pong player in the world, under the influence, but my play got much worse as revealed by playing this guy named Ralph who never looked like he was playing but almost always hit the ball back. Mr. Panic, nickname, was about as close to playing against a backboard as you might find so I could test him with my cocaine abilities and without them. Cocaine slowed down my game, my thinking, my learning and just about everything else other than sex. Mr. Panic wasn't there for that, had he been I might have learned something I didn't want to know about that too. I needed Mr. Panic, who I wasn't attracted to, to teach me this. You need a partner in life right around the,, corner, of the bed,, time that you are learning that there is something other than illusion: there is root canal. There is nothing like a dentist to drill a hole in your illusion. I think it was a dentist who first told me, or showed me, that there isn't a Santa Clause. You need relationship at that tender point, once you have discovered that you are the boss, to let you know that you are not so that you will be ready for a visit from the real boss: truth.

Illusion is a drug: it puffs your performance out of perspective, un-Einsteins science and un-Heideggers philosophy into a world of absolute negotiation.[6] Yes, you create your own nightmare not your own reality. Einstein knew this, that is why he didn't wear any socks. I know someone who had breakfast with Einstein and he really didn't wear socks and his hair really looked like that and as far as I know he didn't really have any deep personal relationships, by my terms at least not with people, just ones with everything which is no way to go through life because if the truth can't be put to the test on something other than a blackboard, then you don't get to do the next necessary step after finding out that there is a truth, which is to move it from your head to your heart then to the head of another and then to the heart of another. Seduction, sedition, and stealth. It is seduction, not because it is successful, but because there is a primary difference between Head and Heart. The head sometimes says no sometimes yes by the patterns creating an overall motive of defensive maybe. The heart always says yes. If the heart stops saying yes it murmurs or stops saying anything at all.

Each solar year there is a range of greater light days to lesser light days. The sun doesn't have low enough self-esteem to care about this, but the Earth, tilting wildly as it does, gives less light some days than others. The further you are from the latitudinal center of Earth the shorter will be any given light day and the longer will be the darkness until the world turns and Alaska is light nearly all day long. As long as you worship illusion the poles will have their way with you and Polish jokes,

---

[6] Stage One: Shut up about your illusion. Stage Two: Evangelize about your illusion to anyone who won't listen. Stage Three: Discover you are full of shit. Stage Four: Strip yourself bare. Stage Five: Let in whatever shows up carrying nothing. Stage Five: Open to relating. Stage Six: Chorus: "This must be love, love, love" (sung by *Madness*). Stage Seven: Begin again. Remember you have seven bits and these are the stages that fit in them.

such as what you make important, will rule both the light day and the light night as you have to react given that what you have thought and what you have done drag the general coefficient of speed of thinking things here on Earth and the only way that you can catch up is illusionarily.

If you want to help me out you will find the words in my text that aren't really words yet and you will use them, in context, with that confidence or exactly the lack of confidence that you would use real words, so that you convince Webster and in the process make the sort of offbeat ideas I exspouse here onbeat moving them from the headiness of this book to the heart of culture and making both you and your friends more interesting in the process.[7] Any good suggestion probably should contain a bribe, a what is in it for you, so that you don't have to do it just because it is good because to do it just because it is good is a little too much like just taking your medicine, which hopefully as you read this you have outgrown. Especially if you are ready for personal relationship you either have to have outgrown it or be ready too. It is hard to concentrate on life with an ingrown illusion.[8]

If you are going to draw straws to determine the truth you had better make sure that all straws are the same length. In other words: You are handicapped and there is nothing like a good woman or a good man to point this out to you everyday. Courage is having the same one point it out each day, finding the nuances of your nits, like the great apes.

---

[7] Just by reading this book you have become something other than the kind of a person that only an exspouse could appreciate and maybe love. Though your exspouse is a test of some things, tests that must be passed, your currentspouse is the one who holds the power for you.

[8] When you have forgotten what I see you as you have forgotten a lot. When you have forgotten what you see you as you have gained a little. Together, we should be.

Almost Aside: I think that there ought to be a law that everything should wear a label to reveal its ultimate generic level of interaction with human beings. These labels should be in a universal language. A scorpion, and the blonde, should wear a tag that says "ouch" warning of the consequences of getting too close. Each tag should indicate a precise range of safety or intimacy that said tagged one should remain. A rattlesnake should wear a tag that says, "ouch, ouch, yum." The double "ouch" indicating the distance it should be given, striking distance, and the yum because under the right cook's tutelage rattlesnake tastes great. Chocolate éclairs should wear a label that says "yummmmmmmmm" indicating that though they are tasty too many of them will widen your girth. I hesitate to give you more examples though I am sorely tempted. Tempted is "yumouchyumouchyumouch."

I don't want this to become a cut-and-paste book, for aesthetic reasons, nor do I want to get in the way of your creativity.[9] You can do it! You really can do it! (Who says this book isn't motivational?) With some thought and creativity you can come up with a label for anything and everything. With some bravery you can come up with universal labels for the people you know. With perfect introspection you can come up with a label for yourself and with sufficient growth you can move from label to bigger label increasing reward and decreasing downside in a sort of Perpetually More Palatable Direction (PMPD). When you get done with creating the whole label

[9] Can we talk? Would you do me a favor? Would you please get a pen and make a mark in the blank space that is to follow, or write a word should you be so inclined right here   . Thanks. Now if I ever find this book in a used bookstore or someone else reads it they will have a Robinson Crusoe moment after they get over the fact that you wrote in the book they will know that they are not alone and this is worth something isn't it? If there is already a mark in the spot above then you had better not have purchased this book as new, thinking you were alone. Thanks for your company. Now you and I are co-writers.

system genus and species please send it along to me well in advance of implementing it and also let my mediocre face grace the single unit label much as George Washington haunts, and bucks, us today. I long to be Thomas Jefferson, inflation you know.[10]

---

[10] I remain subtly pissed off that the height, length and width of letters isn't used to contain more meaning than the sounds the letters allegedly make. You just can't put an "m" and an "n" side by side and expect them to support the same weight.

CHAPTER 12

Seducing the Iron Maiden[1]

How do you top yesterday? Because when it comes to today, if you are going to have something be good enough, you must not merely call but must always raise. The way to raise is to be present today. That way the exact strains and strings from both past and future will present a guidewire for you to walk on making certain that you neither become too confident nor too insecure on your way up the able. If you handle time when you get around to it you will not walk the cable but be bound by it, which really isn't the point anyway. You need your loved one to receive from your loved two a cuckoo clock not a cherry so that at least you remember who you are in their eyes every hour.

If your song is "I won't grow up, I'll never grow up, I don't want to go to school..."[2] then you are at the door of growing up.

---

[1] Iron maiden—iron lung?

[2] If your theme is "I won't throw up, I'll never throw up, I do want to go to church...," then you are at the door of spirituality and probably already, at least in the worst of times, learned much of what you needed to here on Earth. This goes to show you that when it comes to spirituality your stomach is much more relevant than your mind, and it is. Your heart should kick you in the last stages of earthly delights. The heart continues into spirituality but the stomach plays a very active role too. Butterflies in your tummy means hints of spirituality to come.

You are ready for Freddy, ready for life on Earth. Ready to be fingered by everything and everyone on Earth. Caught in your attempts to escape and returning by your own free will, if for no other reason, than to prove that there isn't one.

What kind of world have you been living in anyway?

It is likely that you perceived the preceding question as rhetorical. Shame on you. Answer it would you?

You need to be more hearty than heady? Yes. Here is a tip: Don't be a good waiter or you may get stuck waiting. If you aren't willing to wait for someone to love please don't wait for anything else either.

What is the all-important difference between rocks and ideas?

Another non-rhetorical question? Rocks are often underground and when they come out of the ground they are soft in relation to what they will be soon. If you are to build a chimney, say, with rocks, you want to break them into whatever shapes you want before they are exposed to air for long. Once they are exposed to air they will break the sculpture. Ideas are rather the opposite. An idea should be teased out from deep within you and never tested on the way out. Once it is out it should begin to soften under your scrutiny and that of those around you who you respect deeply and love. As the idea softens it reveals the contribution that y'all can make to each other as the idea moves from within you to within them. It isn't the idea that matters, unless you are identified with it. It is the opportunity to give an unexamined gift to someone: a risk. If you don't risk in relationship you don't grow in relationship and if you don't grow in relationship you aren't in relationship.

Content is substance and anything you do with the substance once it has left your inner circle is abuse. Substance abuse is hard to quit, and though it will never have you get an A+ it may get you in AA. A+ is the highest possible grade and

AA is a group of people who understand all you don't want to know about yourself: Would you like a light?

The iron maiden is any form that a relationship is fit into. Relationship doesn't fit, it suffocates with rules and it must always expand more rapidly than the two or more people in it would expand on their own. Relationship is to be sufficiently intimate that you risk everything every moment. The purpose of risk is to maximize your use of attention. Too much attention on yourself can have you wither and drown, too much attention on another isn't possible. Splitting attention between you and them is schizophrenia of the healthiest kind.

Don't surround yourself with yourself, move on back two squares. The test for reality or illusion is how something travels between people.[3] If it moves from one to the other, softening and then is reborn within the other, this contributes to its myth of legitimacy, having it move from the toddler stage to that of a full-grown handicap. The only way to find out if something is legitimate is to test it in the market place which means to try and sell it to someone who hasn't an ulterior motive but does have a clue. If your deep personal relationships don't suffer from a primary flaw of not wanting the boat to be rocked or the boot to be given, then you are lucky in deed. You can have someone who, though she is not you, is reading from the same page and providing the best of possible return on your attention investment.

What is a profound similarity between relationship and geometry?

This is not a rhetorical question.

The primary purpose of relationship is to extend the distance between two points in the process of triangulation. The main thing you need to know about anything is whether it is a

---

[3] Put a fork in it: the road, that is.

threat to you or whether not having it will be a threat to you. To know this you must first know how far away it is. Paul Revere was right; the British were coming. Without him to let you know this there could have been trouble. Quality of life for a human being depends on depth and the only way to get depth is to have two points observing one point which is the whole three-pointedness of geometry. The further apart the observing two points are the more accurate a measurement of depth there is. Within thinking there is no depth, because there really is no depth in the brain. The way to create depth is to look at an idea from two very different vantage points. This is difficult to do by yourself and usually results in thinking off. Creating depth is much easier to do with another person and provides the much-value-added benefit of having your readings be more accurate because the two vantage points are farther apart. The very same threat, dispersion of viewpoint, that another offers, is also the benefit, diversion of viewpoint. Raising your tolerance for difference without losing perspective of it will always result, in time, in greater clarity.[4]

Remember side-angle-side and angle-side-angle from geometry? Those were ways of finding out what you didn't know with great accuracy, deducing it specifically from what you did know. The specifically is important here because it is the accuracy of relationships that is their promise and the inaccuracy of relationships that is their hallmark and plague. If you can't get there from here you need to know that as soon as possible. If you can get there from here you need to be able, with great accuracy, to discover what being there would be like

---

[4] Remember that feeling of your nose clearing for the first time after a cold in which it seemed the snot would go on forever? Or that moment in which you noticed and realized at the same time that your best friend really was female and that you liked her in spite of yourself and that that in spite of made you more not less important?

before you go so that if it won't work you don't bother and if you need to bring special clothes you can bring them along.[5]

The shortest distance between two people, hopefully sex, yields the least accuracy. The longer the distance the greater the accuracy and the more likely relationship is to threaten one of your primary illusions: the illusion of security. Also, the more likely you are to forget that the other person exists. If you do that, the two points will be in you, the joke will be on you and the accuracy of triangulation will be no further apart than any two points in your body. Certainly you can have theoretical points anywhere but they will never enhance your accuracy in that they are the first to disappear under pressure. Becoming, not diamonds, but little nuggets of stuckness that fester into cancer or worse.

In the Museum of Natural History there was a "Turn of the Century" room. It was to show what an average kitchen and front room looked like in 1900. The rooms were full-sized replicas behind thick glass. Knowing a guard at the museum helped. One evening I got into one of these rooms only to discover that these were no average rooms. The dishes on the table were glued down as were the cups and the silverware. I am thinking that if, back then, they glued and nailed everything down there might have been much less clean-up necessary. But things probably weren't as useful either. The couch was invisibly nailed down, so were the napkins and the books on a table, as was the table.

I realized that there is a tendency, due I imagine to insecurity, to glue and nail nearly everything down in relationship:

---

[5] I have heard that this very smart but tipsy man used to sell cars. Dressed as a mechanic he sold many cars, dressed as a car salesman he sold few. Dressed as a Catholic priest he sold quite a few but only to non-Catholics. Will you like your savior? I hope so for your sake because eternity is a long time and you really ought to leave with the one you spent the most time with.

remember chastity belts? I don't really call it chastity unless you have the option to mess around.

Would you rather get something or have it given willingly? We live far from any convenience store.

Why is it that being buried together seems so romantic? Maybe because it is as close as two people can get for a long time. Relationship isn't supposed to be predictable; it is supposed to soften all your no's and soften all of the other person's no's, not in a pretend way but really. Seduction, in relationship, looks like an absence of reaction and a willingness to look at part of you as part of them and part of them as part of you, leading to having all of them be all of you and all of you be all of them.

Seduction looks a little like always having to say that you are sorry. Scrutiny is a particular kind of attention that lends credence to intimacy. Observation is the greatest aphrodisiac there is. You don't need help but you do need company. Relationship really should be deeper than auction or professional ball. The highest bidder has no clout here. The winner in relationship is who can open more, modeling out opening for the other person. As I have stated earlier, there is no room in relationship for preferences of any kind. Initial stages of relationships are dismantling, probably unilaterally, preferences which were only put there for defense. The best defense is no defense at all.

With triangulation, if you lie about something, both of you lose. Geometry loses its sacredness and you two too. Something, everything, is really closer or further than it seems. Your readings are off and somebody is to blame for the inaccuracy. The two known points of a triangulation must be known by their flexibility (ability to flex) and their respect (ability to look again). Without these, the rigidity in one moment misses the possible, having regular speech suffer from the Doppler effect as each of you run for different cover at the same time. Since thought can move faster than the speed of sound but not much faster than the speed of light you won't really survive in a relationship based on babble.[67]

---

[6] I have timed it. It took my true love less than a minute, sixty seconds, to begin raking me over the coals after double orgasmic sex. At that point she could have been using her mouth for anything else, even kissing, but she wasn't. If you don't leave them breathless they will probably be talking.

[7] When your point is to blame their point for any inaccuracy you really miss the point of relating, which is....

CHAPTER 13

A Very Good Day: Every Day

What is a good day? I am the same amount of tired at the end of the day if I have done a little, a lot or none at all. To be otherwise is to play a mean time-bound game, without oneself anywhere around, in which even the preponderance of players doesn't justify. Intelligence is a day with this, diversion a day with that. If you can hold yourself up to something as though to measure, you will soon not be that different than that which you measure or are measured by. In other words: There is nothing which makes you tired. You are just tired when you are tired. Thinking that there is something that makes you tired makes me tired. Not really, but as long as your causes and effects are reasonable, they can be sold to any lowest common denominator waiting in the market place. They can be spread simply by similarity.

"It just shows up in my head. It just shows up in my head. It just shows up in my head. I had nothing to do with it, I was just following orders." Any idea that you have that you played any role in anything is at best superfluous, on average illusionary and at worst, your word for it, delusionary. "Do you promise to tell the truth the whole truth and nothing but the truth?" C'mon, is this some kind of joke in the Hall of Justice?

Can I tell you a secret, a top secret, a secret that is unsafe in the hands or heads of anyone who hasn't read this far? It just shows up in your head. It just shows up in your head. It just shows up in your head. (This statement must always be said in threes. It is a tribute to Johann Strauss, the "waltz-king:" that was the dance for then this is the dance for now kind of thing.) These three must always be weighted roughly the same too, and it helps if they are equivalent.

I am the same amount of tired at the end of the day if I have done a little, a lot or none at all. To be otherwise is to play a mean time-bound game, without oneself in which even the preponderance of players doesn't justify.[1]

Intelligence: A day without it is clearly and concisely a day not worth having lived. Intelligence is the lubricant that has the seconds glide into minutes, the minutes glide into hours and the hours move slowly into daze. If you ain't tiptoeing you just are being way too obvious and being on tiptoe is the best way to get picked for the basketball team. Intelligence is a very special kind of chemical lubrication that bridges the gap in the synapses in your head and hands. The heart powers the brain and when it is sufficiently open it releases a chemical called WD-50 which has the synapses snap it up and take notice.[2] Without this chemical thinking isn't worth doing; without it, thinking will always be some form, unfinished and proud of its finish, diverting you from anything worthwhile and to anything not worthwhile. To intelligence, "you can't get there from here" are fighting words. You have to be able to handle relationship to a fairly high degree before you can tackle intelligence, otherwise

---

[1] Do you ever have déjà vu, have déjà vu, have déjà vu? Is there an echo in here, here, here? Holding a stutterer to the letter of the law is more difficult than holding a good liar in your accounting department.

[2] It is fifty because fifty is the magic number that is flunking and yet exactly half way between the devil and the deep blue sea: it is see level. At fifty percent probability you have the most influence you will ever have, the opportunity to make or break, create or destroy. WD-50 is little known but wildly underrated.

being smart will just make you smart. As in "that smarts." It will hurt you to know what is beyond your grasp. Your head and your hands have to get lubricated at the same time otherwise you will just suffer from Smart Blonde Syndrome (SBS). Have you noticed that smart blondes are always alone and dumb ones never are? Maybe they know something that you don't, the knowing of which gets in their way.

You are going to have to get smarter as you get related. If you don't you will always be behind the curve and perpetually striking out.[3] Intelligence has two primary directives: One is speed and the other is expansion; the third is connection. The easiest way to run a four-minute mile is to get a broken stopwatch and time yourself with it. That way it doesn't matter how fast you run as long as you keep tabs on the watch. Intelligence dictates that it might make more sense just to time yourself while ignoring, to a great extent the distance, and stop the watch at slightly less than four minutes figuring that you should be paid extra, overtime, for anything in excess of your target. Laziness has you hire a personal trainer, college-style intelligence has him exercise for you. I don't like riding in the car. There are few things that I hate more. But I am willing to go the long way around just to miss the campus. Even the co-eds don't cut the mustard on this one.

Many years ago I ran a retail store. One evening Bill, the Kmart manager trainee from a few stores down, invited me to go with him to a marketing seminar at a local university. It wasn't a date. We went and heard the man who wrote the book talk about marketing and watched the people who read the book listen as though they were listening to the man who wrote the book. There was an informal get-together after the big

---

[3] If the bat is the ball the ball is a curve with a radar-assisted commitment to a no-hitter.

meeting, sort of a *round-table* discussion where the man who wrote the book would know everything and the rest of us would notice how much we were missing the boat by:[4] did I mention that this event was held at the local university, that I have since learned to avoid? Never wanting to miss the chance to be legitimately informal, Bill and I went to the *round-table*, which as it turns out was oval, a rather extreme oval but not so big that we couldn't see the crisp untested edge of this marketer's philosophy, even from the most obtuse of elliptical points: he made.

Bill managed a bunch of people, he ran a successful store and dealt with many customers on a daily basis, he stocked shelves when necessary, stacked shelves around Christmas, and on this particular evening he asked a question: "What would you suggest for getting the turns in my store from the three and a half that we are at now to four?"

Turns means the number of times that the entire inventory is replaced in a year. You never really develop much respect for a turn until you have put each item on the shelf yourself, rung each item up, put each item in a bag and seen a certain percentage of the items come back for refunds, or at least been responsible for the people who do this.

It has taken years of pretend therapy to forget exactly what the man who wrote the book said. Suffice it to say that it was short, ugly and mean. He pounced on the practicality of Bill and ripped it to shreds. He indicated, in no certain terms, that not only was Bill's question the least likely to be answered in this century but that Bill, by the pragmatic nature of his question should not have been allowed into the meeting. "Who let you in?" he sliced. I didn't see a bouncer at the door, these silly little students couldn't have bounced anybody so it must be that the

---

[4] You can't miss the boat, you are the boat. Oar, you can't miss the boat you are the boat.

man who wrote the book was the bouncer, deciding as educators often do what was worth thinking about and what was not.[5]

Intelligence: Anything is worth thinking about as long as you think about it more quickly than anyone has ever thought about it before, place it in a new context, fertilize it, grace it with just slightly more attention than it deserves and then turn it out to pasture with an immense lack of effort. The first test for intelligence is the hand, the second is somebody else. You have to start with somebody else which is why we dealt with relationship in the previous chapter. The hand is a much tougher master than somebody else.[6]

Being smart is to intelligence as being rich is to printing real money. Intelligence is a matter of letting go of energy, while being smart is a matter of restricting it. When you hire a player piano for your party you will be serving at least day-old rolls.

We don't put much stock in intelligence because it inspires such profound creativity that it scares us. I put myself in the same boat as you in the preceeding phase just because I like you. If I didn't like you so much I would have put you in the boat with other such yous and you could have set up your own university with the only threat being the wolf to the sheep's skin. You like things rather like they are only a little different and if that weren't the case you would embrace change on the first time around and not keep looking the gift horse in the no's.

You cannot raise your intelligence without raising the intelligence of everyone around you. You can't get paid for raising their intelligence because then you won't really be in favor of it raising except within the confines of ownership. If the people around you don't get smarter they will get relatively

---

[5] Sort of a *man in the yellow hat* mentality, coming after it has happened and inadvertently saving the day. I am partial to white hats myself.

[6] I knew a bachelor, confirmed, who didn't date. He had a picture of his hand, in a frame, on his desk at work...and at play.

dumber making you only look smarter and not really be smarter. If you can't build the entire universe in real time and explain anything and how it works cross context, then you need to raise your intelligence. Intelligence and security are at odds and intelligence and insecurity are never found within four miles of each other. As you get smarter everything will make more sense to you. Déjà vu is a hint of expressed intelligence.[1] There is nothing that you haven't already done and nothing that you haven't already learned. You can burn through this take-home test with eyes closed but why would you? Intelligence is about matching what is in your head with the compliment of what is in your surroundings in real time so that you are left with nothing, the vacuum of which, you can clean any surface of dust or clutter and have a place to put anything that you create.

We had a really good singer/song writer perform a concert here about a month ago. I will not tell you his name because he isn't famous yet and I don't want to hasten him on the way there. Do you have any idea how many people have read this book and how special a person it makes you to have done so? *Aside:* You want to always get into the smallest minorities that you can fit in because that is where your energy will be the least diluted and your intelligence the most practically appreciated and your ability to generally harass the most outsiders will be the greatest. But, the performer said, "It is a good song if writing it, playing it and listening to it all take the same amount of time." It is the excess fat that needs to be cut away, in real time. I have spoken to Dan Millman, author of *Way of the Peaceful Warrior*, a number of times and e-mailed him more often than that. On one call I asked, "Dan," (do you mind if I call him Dan), "did you enjoy writing your most recent very thick but dry book?" "No, it was one of the worst experiences of my life." he

---

[1] I used déjà vu in the last chapter too, remember?

said. "How do you expect people to enjoy reading it if you didn't enjoy writing it?" I asked. (I wished Dan hadn't said "no;" if you can still say no and are pretending to be spiritual, you can only be fooling yourself, unless you are an author and then you can be fooling a lot of people all the way to the bank.) He didn't really have an answer. You must be having a riot about now reading this. I am writing with such aggression on the keyboard just to get this out that I imagine this is about as close to giving birth as a man can get. "Ouch," it hurts but it hurts really good. Dan enjoyed writing *Way of the Peaceful Warrior*, you might enjoy reading it. It isn't smart but it is sweet.[8]

One of my basic rules in life is to not ever get so busy that I don't have all the time in the world to think. Another basic rule is never to think more than I neck. Thinking without necking is the exclusion of the hand as the game turns to "Mind Only Need Apply."

You are much smarter than you think you are, you are infinitely intelligent. Schooling, most of it, tries to raise your smarts at the cost of your intelligence. Intelligence overtime, now that is funny, provides waitless wisdom that stretches

---

[8] Sometimes it will raise your intelligence just to pretend that things are opposites that really might not be. To consider sweetness the opposite of intelligence might not be as far-fetched as you might think. To consider anger the opposite of humor may just make you smarter. If you can play this little game with opposites you may as well try it with synonyms. Who said that two things needed to be equal for you to act as if they are equal? "Act as if" should to some degree be everyone's mantra as they bring head and hand together in a gesture of raising the intelligence on the plain to a life-sustaining level. You will get much smarter just reading this book, but you will probably get angry too. I suggest that if you have any control over anything at all that you balance with one foot on anger and one foot on humor so that at least by the end of this chapter you no longer take yourself or anything that you perceive yourself to be as serious as it was before.

patients to the breaking point leading you back to the present.[9] You have no idea how seductive the unthought is. The most immediate and most enjoyable path to seduction, the conversion of someone's no to a yes, is intelligence. Well, maybe love is faster but real love isn't enjoyable at all. Intelligence jumps the hurdle and knows that it is there, love just goes right through it without jumping or knowing it's over. Love with intelligence creates the hurdle so that you can have something useful to mesh hand and head, and unlimited practice with unlimited patience.

Getting faster is usually the result of one of two things or both: It is the result of letting go of something that you were holding on to or splitting something that you were holding on to into something like equal pieces. If they aren't something like equal you form an immediate dependence on the larger one or the smaller one depending on how optimistic or pessimist you are or how open to winning or losing you are. Speeding up is not a relative event, it is not context dependent; if it is you are still stopping to take readings on your surroundings, those readings defining where you are and leaving an obvious schedule of where you have been to justify yourself should you ever show up in court. You need to move off on your own, pushing off nothing and moving without preference to direction. When you move non-directionally you will statistically, most of the time, be forced out of the horizontal domain that most humans get paid for, derive security from, and whine about and move into some degree of angular vertical which has any thought threaten existence. When you move vertically you get smarter without

---

[9] I think that doctors should have telephones in their offices that patients who are waiting can use to place long distance calls while they wait for the doctor. Given the decline in phone rates they may want to work their way up to expensive, if healthy, buffets.

time passing which presents enough speed to have anything be entertaining. At that point you become the seducer because the no's have no place to take root.

Have you ever looked at the plants that live on a very steep hillside? They are the grateful ones, the tenacious ones, the ones which understand the gravity of the situation and are in momentary contact with mortality. They grow as fast as they can and live as fully as they can: this is the payoff of moving without preference to direction and only to speed. Certainly it makes them less majestic than a redwood but it has them provide you a hand or foot hold as you are climbing or falling perhaps saving your life and intelligence at the same time. They also provide you a perfect metaphor to rap each of your thoughts in. For speed,, to not be too threatening, as you raise your intelligence, you will need to hold on so that you can get the benefit of letting go. As you raise your intelligence there will be nothing more relevant to you than trust, oddly, the subject of the next chapter.[10]

---

[10] Catch and release depends on that order. Catch what you can, release what you catch and enjoy the process. When you release less than you catch you end up with dated inventory, the worst kind, bad enough to spoil.

Trust

You don't get to die until you have left enough signs of your foolishness around for others to derive entertainment value from as they learn raising their intelligence from your accidental inspiration. If you die before this your lifetime doesn't count, your attention accounts don't balance and you may have to serve another lifetime, reincarnally speaking, "for extortion."

If there is someone who is too big to be tackled you don't have a football game, you have a season. If there is anything on Earth too big to tackle you don't have a life, just a shopping list of problems partially filled upon your death. If you can't tackle something alone, that is an obvious time for teammates: relationship. Teammates force the issue, gezundheit, of trust. If you don't trust them they aren't teammates. If you can't turn way more than one of their no's to yes you shouldn't be trusting them. Trust is never to be based on performance because like any good mutual fund buyer knows "past performance is no indication of future performance." If you can seduce them, you might be able to trust them; if you cannot seduce them their own peril dominates your own life.

We had a good friend of ours build a carport for us. We saw a design we liked over a walking path at a state park, you may want to stop by there and see it sometime—it is really neat. He built it, painted it and was well on his way to putting a roof on it when I walked out, stood under it and realized, without really knowing it, that something was wrong. I made the smallest talk I could which seemed to raise his spirits and maybe his height. "What am I doing hanging around here?" I wondered. Then it hit me. He had built the foundation very well, he had moved a lot of clay to allow deep feet. He had bought really fancy beams to allow the twenty-three feet to be spanned without inspiring much hope or death in those passing under, he had done a typically excellent job inspiring confidence in almost every way, except one.[1] He forgot the horizontal pieces that run at a forty-five degree angle supporting the frame of the roof on the vertical wooden pillars that compose the height of the structure. Without these the whole structure could flex laterally which in some circles may have appeared to be progress but in this case made it much more likely that in the case of strong wind the whole carport would have fallen lengthdumb[2] right on the ground. He had inadvertently built a kind of folding garage. Remember that in the last chapter I spoke of intelligence being composed of movement and the reflection of connection and most of said connections being angular, either up or down but few sideways. That is not exactly how I put it but that is what I mean now by how I put it then.

Aside: I have heard redundantly that you can't step in the same river twice. I don't really get the step in the river thing but I think I get the message and what I just said that I said resembles what I really said enough that we could easily seduce you into thinking that what I have just said is just a later

---

[1] My grandma used to say, "Don't even date anyone you wouldn't be willing to stand under in a wind storm." Or, "If you wouldn't trust the house they built to live in don't move in on, with, them." My grandmother, married very, very happily for over fifty years, thought that it was really neat that people could try living together without being married as long as they didn't do it around her.

[2] Sometimes seen in the company of widthdumb, too fat or too skinny, and wisdumb, obvious and heightdumb.

chapter enhancement of what I said before, because if it isn't, you might be a bit bashful about reading on. I am getting to the point, the problem being, that you can't derive, drive, there from here, but that certainly isn't going to stop us from trying or getting there. Glad you read the aside, "good."

He put in the horizontals and we have all lived happily ever after. I trusted him before he put in the supports, I trust him now too. I trust him to do exactly what he does and to never do what he doesn't do which is, to me, the most secure kind of trust that someone can have without maintenance. You may say, "Good for me." but I would retort, "Good for you too." because, and this I am sure of, if I can do it you can do it and improve on it. While it is more fun without supports it is more secure with them. You have to be able to enjoy anything that you build with them, focusing and creating attention as you go, until you put the supports on and the supports keep the ground in place under the carport, freeing your attention to go wherever it will.

Trust allows your attention to go wherever it will and where it won't too. Trust is finding out what you get within close proximity of getting it rather than deciding what you want before you get it only to either not get what you want, frown, or get what you want, fake smile, only to find out that nearly immediately you want something else, double-frown unnoticed (motivational).

To trust you have to base your wants on what you have, but, and this is an attractive little but, you have to in no way identify with the support or the specific location or function of my carport. In other words, you have to find the fallen carport and the dented Mercedes as interesting as the beautifully crafted carport over the beautifully crafted unscratched Mercedes. At one level your trust is just a matter of reducing adjectives: At another level, it is the ability to disappear anything. If you are intent on features, adjectives, you will not notice the things themselves. If you are intent on the things themselves you will miss yourself, and everybody else. You have paid dearly for adjectives: you have paid way more for the fast, shiny, new, sporty, convertible car than for the "car," than for the contribution it makes to what you perceive your value to be. You have tried to modify through the modifications that which you deem constant which is always a losing battle and fully justifies your playing smaller in the future. You must rid yourself of adjectives prior to ridding yourself of adverbs. Your preferences contain adjectives that haunt your self-esteem building, as it were, a past based self-esteem. Historically speaking, you are either really wonderful terrible or somewhere in between; your future need not be a version of any of these.

Basing trust on evidence gets you into trouble but will never get you out. Everyday-trust isn't quick enough. You have to have every-moment trust. Evidence is always historical so, as neat as it would seem, and as often as it is used, it just doesn't prove diddly. The present has its drawforwards, seeking evidence only has its drawbacks, otherwise every courtroom in the land would be as inspirational to a citizen as Picasso is to an artist. It would also be as daunting to a criminal as Picasso ought to be daunting to an artist, or as it is intended to be. Leaving the present is a criminal act, though it only becomes an offense when relationship is involved.[3] It is the father of them all and trust without evidence is far enough along the way to love without object. That is enough victory to be celebrated for one or more lifetimes: (John 12:14:16).

It is never too early to call a bluff although you may want to wait until there is at least rent money in the pot to do so, though each moment you wait makes it more likely that you

---

[3] Isn't it sort of sickfunny that if only you are concerned it is called a victimless crime? I guess they think that at some level you can't count.

will forget that it is a bluff and fold right when you shouldn't have. If you forget that somebody else is bluffing you may fold prematurely. If you forget that you are bluffing you are the best bluffer of all. It is all a matter of direction of attention and it is all a matter of that.

There is an implicit relationship between mortality and trust that will have to be exhumed for you to be liberated from nonexistence.[4] Trust has to start with death because it is the thing you can be most sure of. There is no part of life that is as certain as death but you distrust death and somehow, the peril of a lifetime, you at least pretend to trust life. Does this strike you as at least a glancing blow to self-esteem worth looking at? We pretend to care about the dead as we abuse the living. Until we can appreciate the living as much as we pretend to the dead we will be a mortriarcle culture.

Mortriarcle has to do with a culture based on death rather than patriarchal which is a culture based on dicks or matriarchal which is a culture based on her. Mortriarcle could also refer to a culture based on mortar but since there has never really been one of those and almost every culture is based on death let's pick the death meaning the birth of this new word. If you aren't convinced try this, repeat after me: Mortar is the stuff that holds things together and life is the process of breaking things apart, or basic training for life is putting things together so that you can break them apart so whether we pick the bricklayer version or the death version it all goes to the same place in the end and all meaning is too short-term and long-winded to be worth bothering with anyway.

---

[4] There is biography, which is someone writing about you. There is autobiography, which is you automatically writing about your favorite subject and there is autopsygraphy which is the last story you ever told in the presence of someone who thought you were already dead.

Christ, no![5] Hold your breath and read on until you don't understand something. This is a good test as to whether something is of value or not based on breathing. If you don't run into something that you don't understand within the cycle of a breath you are holding on to something which has life just become a preparation for the big letting go: death. Death with a capital "D" is the root of all trust. If you don't think it will all work out in the end you are bound to try and get involved in all sorts of things not trusting them to turn out. The more things you try and interfere with, the more you will identify with distrust and the more of a liar you will become about the very nature of things and people. Trust death. Overkill is anything that ends a life not worth living, trust me though I have no experience of this.

When you can trust death you discover that no part of life is really that bad. It is better to have trusted often and been wrong some of the time than never to have trusted at all. Trust, like so many impossible nominalizations, is impossible simply because where it lives has been misidentified. You go over to where trust is supposed to live and you don't find anything but dishonesty there: in others. If you were the only dishonest person in the world it would seem that you could really get ahead, but think about it, it wouldn't really work out that way. If you were the only honest person in the world it would seem that it really wouldn't work out, but think about it, it might not really turn out that way. If there were a whole lot of people some of whom were honest some of the time and others who were dishonest some of the time and there was a third group, judges, who were to determine which was which, you couldn't

---

[5] That was good, that was great: God's first-born son, I'm afraid it's too late. That must be good, that must be bad, when it comes to religion we've all been had. That must be bad, that must be worse: it's the end of my rhyme or the end of this verse.

afford the anguish or legal bills: welcome to Earth.[6]

Trust is located within you. It has nothing to do with naïveté any more than high jumping has anything to do with walking. The more you know the more you know that things aren't what they seem and the harder it is to trust the size things you can think about. Trust starts at each edge of what you can see and sort of sneaks up on the middle. If it is otherwise it isn't trust. Every inch of gained ground from one side must be matched with equal though often opposite lost ground on the other. You can't get there from here takes on a very different meaning when you are already home. When you were born you were a creature of trust. It wasn't long until the gods around you created sufficiently impossible worlds that you just didn't want to trust anymore. Heck, they said one thing and did another as though it was their daily devotional. They put you in petrifyingly perfect double-binds, and that was just until dad got home. Then with his arrival double-binds squared made life only tolerable when one of the gods was choking the other one so that only one could yell at a time.

Trust is an excursion into the poetry of life. It is being seduced by nothing in the face of overwhelming evidence, knowledge, arousal, tears, risk and fear. It is converting the obtuse to the unrecognized and back again all in the name of fun. Everything is purposeful and believing in that will justify almost anything. Trust is unfinished love not yet ready to be spread around. Trust is an individual team sport that has your speed save you just in the nick without time and have you open when you would have closed and close when you would have opened. Trust is the first glimpse of spirituality in that it is your first real contact with the power of nothing over everything.

---

[6] This is the sign that appears at the gates of Heaven. It is a little test for nostalgia: hint: Don't balk.

Spiritual Seduction

Emily, I'm her father, had a best blanket when she was small. I am her best blanket now which makes me about the luckiest person on Earth. She is fourteen as I write this. Her best blanket had a ribbon border around it and she focused on one corner in particular. She would flip her little third and fourth fingers of her right hand over and stick them in her mouth with the blanket held up by her thumb. When she was in this position nothing else was needed. She now twists me around her little finger to get the same effect. That blanket gets as worn as any idea that you take everywhere with you. We washed it occasionally realizing that each washing reduced its lifetime. *Aside:* I once tried this approach in life but soon smelled so bad that I had too specific a reason why others avoided me. I sewed up the corner many times, keeping it on the blanket as best I could. Finally it was too much: what had started as a blanket looked much more like a rag. I cut off the best corner of the best blanket and sewed it onto a new blanket. I gave it to her, wondering if I would be able to afford the therapy bills. She flipped her fingers, thumbed the corner and all was right with the world ever after.

One day she didn't need the blanket anymore, now she just trusts. The trust from within is not evidentiary as I have said but it is based on skills to a certain point and from there just on enjoyment. If you can be sufficiently fast to often influence how things turn out, or appear to, and enjoy however they turn out, the rest of the time there is nothing to worry about. The role of expectation and preparation in this process cannot be underemphasized. The role of flexibility, relationship and intelligence cannot be overstated; flexibility in that there is a nearly infinite bank of possible responses, relationship, in that you have someone you can trust when you are wise enough to not trust yourself, and speed, in that you often meet what is coming from where it is going, are enough to inspire competence without confidence. Emily has all these, you do too, though it might take a little trust to find them.

CHAPTER 15

Orgasm

If you like the crust better than the fruit you may be tempted to bake your own pie, but when you do you may as well save on electricity by sliding your own goose into the oven with the pie so they can cook at the same time. When you bake your own pie you will ignore the recipe, which probably worked, and add more crust and less fruit until you have a very crusty pie that you can pretend to like all by yourself. You miss the fruit though, you long for the fruit, though the less fruit you have the better you think you like it. Nostalgia: "I can remember when I made this with fruit." "This is an old family recipe, if not a favorite." "I call it crust pie, do you like it, do you need some water?"

You fail to notice the pattern as with years of therapy, "Let them eat cake," squeaks your therapist, you phase fruit back in, tipping the scales back all the way past a good pie to all fruit. Someone visits you, a chance for relationship, when your mix of crust and fruit is around 50/50 and nominates you for the county fair, but by the time the season to be fair rolls around you are excessively fruity and taking a number at a new therapist's office.

Orgasm alone is a cherry pie with only crust and no cherries at all. While you still know it is cherry pie a stranger finds you stranger than you seek to be found and you remain that way until an orgasm seeks to break the door down, and hopefully it does but you certainly aren't going to help.

The Rolling Stones said something like, "Orgasm is the moment you can't cheat life." I remember this line from the everlasting, old favorite, movie, *Sympathy for the Devil*. I won't be seeing the movie anytime soon preferring the memory of it. I take great solace, and get some historical burns, from the fact that not only are things not what they used to be but I am not what I used to be so things and I have sort of taken a sabbatical from "used to be" together. We were pals.

The Stones, of course, were wrong. With a little bit of practice and even the slightest spiritual ascension you can learn how to have orgasm be a negotiable event, and while this initially takes the fun out of it, like so many things, later it gets added back in in substantially greater proportions.

Orgasms are the highest form of physical yes, short of death. When you have a one-to-one balance between no's and orgasms in your life you will have united mind and body and be able to play from that moment on. Anytime you have more no's than orgasms you are theoretically getting in your own way while knowing better. If you didn't know better you could plead ignorance, a popular plea, but since you do know better you are a criminal and the only way to redeem yourself is to have more orgasms. Get coming.

While more orgasms may not be something to seek, orgasms are a good indicator on an earthly path and a fair indicator on a spiritual path. You will know that you are at a much higher level when you just can't come down to orgasm, that is the spiritual part. For most people they have to rise to an orgasm, a spiritual person must fall, the faster the better into it.

Death is the only higher form of physical yes than orgasm. Luckily, you don't get to die until you have left enough signs of your foolishness around for others to derive entertainment value from as they learn raising their intelligence from your accidental inspiration to intentional second, third and fourth coming. If you die before this your lifetime doesn't count, your attention accounts don't balance and you may have to serve another lifetime, reincarnally speaking, "for lack of sufficient extortion."

Until you can have every emotion known to womankind with no outside stimuli in a minute or less while looking into your lover's eyes, you will just have to depend on anything that wanders your way. And why not?

Your entire life can be lived in a lifetime, a month, a minute, an hour or just too long. It can be lived or it can be ignored; the difference is in attention, yours not mine. Somewhere between your head and your heart is a little nearly invisible spark waiting to burst into flame to burn down the remnants of what you have called you and ignite the possibilities of what I call me.

I need to reach out to you more often than I reach back in because then when I am gone I will still live over there. You get to do the same thing not for any ulterior motive other than that you can.

If you went to the garden store and saw seed packets with your picture on them would you want those seeds in your garden? Would you hang out around the display of your seeds and find out if anybody is buying or would you grab a handful of your own seeds and try and sell them to particular, interesting looking people around the store? If your answer was another other than selling them around the store, it is likely that unlike a tumbleweed you have not traveled nearly enough places leaving parts of yourself to haunt you later and point up the degree of "I'll take responsibility to mothering or fathering that thing" you live with. There, comes, comes, a time in life when the only way you can see a deep enough impression of yourself in the world is by way of the echo of an orgasm called a child. Get a load of how much it looks like me when it is young. Imagine how persistent it will be when it acts like me when it is older.[1]

If you rise with the water you have to depend on your lightness or displacement. If you can rise on your own you get to do anything.

When I was little we went to the Sault Locks in Sault Sainte Marie, Michigan.[2] This is the place where greatness meets greatness a little off balance. It is only when one is higher than the other that it is time to go to minimal lengths to even out this in difference. I can't quite believe the way that life imitates life giving us an opportunity to live again each moment, pretending, it keeps daring, that there is more to life than we will ever know. If a kid treated you this way on the playground you would call him a bully, but you might also be forced to befriend him just to get by. What if you are a writer and synchronicity isn't enough? What if you are a physicist and find no penance in Chaos Theory? What if when you have a chapter to write each person you meet that day gives you a line from it and all you need to do is organize a little bit and remember to enjoy your day? What if when you are stepping up on a curb you misjudge slightly catching the toe of your girlfriend's sandal, trip and rise? Until you can suspend the laws of physics you will be stuck stretching the laws of man: The Fall: again. Spirituality is your calling and you just want to sit there and negotiate. This doesn't mean that you can stop brushing your teeth: we are clear about the intent of the dentist and we all know about their suicide rate. I have always been afraid of

---

[1] Sometimes I think that Robin Hood and Father Hood are cousins, but that is only when I exaggerate my own lack of worth and consider that I might be sufficiently poor to benefit from my father's, passing on, of some wisdom to my son.

[2] I'm thinking the whole idea of locks could be very useful for relating. If it helps two great lakes get along it could work with too little waters like us. We could step down or step up as was needed if we weren't so committed to being inclined.

getting hit by a stray bullet in a dentist's office ever since I learned that they were armed.

Isn't it funny that just a little offset greatness is enough to impede transportation, communication and transcendence? Unless, of course, you didn't know that. If you didn't know that I guarantee that you knew something else much less useful. From above they just look like a bunch of great lakes connecting things. Not so obviously the chain, linear, is a problem separated by the solution which moves ever stronger to the next problem. You won't run out of this chain while you are alive so there is nothing, really, that you can lose. This life is too easy, you can follow it with your eyes closed if you are willing and with the lights off if your constitution is a bit too weak to keep them closed. You move from one link to the other and from one layer to another.

It is very painful to not be much alive and be here on Earth. It is way, way, more painful to be here on Earth, living. In a good way. If you have the mental pain last even one moment less or one moment more than the physical pain you have indulged something that isn't. Early termination results in inexplicable phantom pain that can't be cured psychologically but existentially. An element of that cure is buying things like time and space that make life on Earth intolerable. Late termination enters the area of delusion which is spreading sterile ideas under the guise of darkness to anyone disinterested enough in themselves to be what you would in that impoverished state call a friend. Either way you are damned and while the idea of hydro-electric may be good with rivers, psycho-electric just builds too much of an unsustainable backlog in the present.[3] You will get busy not dealing with what you should be dealing with and have no time for what you really should be UP to.

Everything you do is an attempt to balance off your mental world of no with the physical world of yes. This, and everywhere else, is where seduction comes in, goes out and hangs around. An orgasm contains very little know, but that is because it is physical. A heartbeat too contains nearly no no. Every thought that you have, by definition, since it is only a thought and not yet an actuality, contains more no than yes. Theory is all gathered around no because no is its basis. The thought of taking a cold shower is one thing, taking a cold shower is another. Taking a cold shower seems a cure for lack of orgasm but it isn't a long-term cure and it will never be the same as anything other than it: not exactly.

It is when a thought tips the scales to more yes than no that you legitimately don the construction hat and put up the construction signs. An orgasm is an upset, sadness, though possibly very pleasant, is a downset. Every emotion is defined entirely by a specific mix of yes and no, with upsets having more yes than downsets but not necessarily more yes than no. Every upset and every downset is offered for a limited time. Take advantage of it now, it is a blues light special. It just seems very blue and not very light and not special at all if it is a downset. If it is an upset it seems temporary, ephemeral and transient. If it is a downset it seems it will last forever as it has become the status resting quo.

Rationalizing at the moment of orgasm is impossible and the longer after orgasm you don't rationalize the more fully you have used the physical yes of orgasm appropriately. Orgasm is an attempt to purge the system by overload.

Pardon me, there is a knock at the door, I will be right back.

---

[3] There is a reason they don't use the locks to generate electricity. One reason is that the imbalance is forcefully evened, taking energy to even what would even in time and number two is: when it comes to imbalance you could benefit from it if you were patient enough to let the storm determine when you get electricity but already always waiting people don't want to wait more no matter how much sense it makes. People's greatest fear is life getting too good, and it just might so watch it.

I'm back. It was Wilhelm Reich dropping off his version of the Yellow Pages. I knew that at some point he would write something people wouldn't burn. I can hardly wait to stick some of the pages of that book together. Neat of him to come at a time like this. He is always we'll come here.

Flirting will purge the system by degrees, a baby-bit at a time. Love purges it by inviting everything in. Orgasm purges it by two hands clapping very loudly without sufficient reason present to put out the fire. Orgasm is a balancing at nearly light speed. A spring storm washes its way to the east, scouring your world. An orgasm always moves from north to south taking with it anything and making the Secretary of Defense an obviously unfilled job position. If you are always orgasming you have nothing to hide. If you are never orgasming you have nothing to seek. "You have nothing to fear but fear itself:" John Kennedy said that.[4] I think, despite puffed up press stories to the contrary, that he wasn't having enough orgasms.

A couple did one of our workshops recently. Their particular pretense was that he wanted sex and she didn't. They were young, delightful and not too vital. Head was winning the race to the bedroom; "Too busy," head said and heart just beat in the background. If I have learned one thing it is that whatever the conners say is happening isn't and whatever they say isn't might be. They had three kids so obviously at some point they had sex. I suggested that they put a large pad with a running, hopefully, tally outside their bedroom. It is nice to have a scoreboard, maybe they could get local merchants to contribute to the cost of paper and pen in return for a small add. They posted the number of times they made love that week for anyone who passed near their bedroom to see. There is nothing like adding spectators to increase performance. They will learn that it isn't that he wants it and she does it. On the next level in,

---

[4] Of course he didn't. Winston did, but I suspect that it really doesn't matter.

she wants it and he doesn't. On yet the next level, it will be somehow different than that. Wandering through the Sexual Haul of Fame, I caught both your picture and my reflection re membering[5] all the good times I have had as a way of bringing us down from the great times. If orgasm doesn't become the anti-climax then you aren't staying sufficiently present all day and especially during sex. Foreplay is being present all day so that it is much more likely that you are present, AT THE TIME. The grim reaper is available for cutting lesser crops in his spare time. When orgasm comes unexpectedly, and you notice it coming, aren't you two the lucky one?

---

[5] Re membering is a delicate procedure not to be undertaken lightly in that you may not do it just right and if you don't, you are bound to do it just wrong. Sometimes you are just bound to do it because the pain is too much so you don't do it accurately which, when dealing with members is pretty scary stuff at least to this guy.

Trust and Decisions: Damned if You "I Do"

Trust comes unexpectedly. If you have no choice there is only trust. If you have choice trust looks like temptation. Some friends of ours and Judson (alias: son age nine, mine) were considering a sleepover at their house. They couldn't make up their so-called minds. I explained how we make decisions around here. The explanation went something like this: "We don't really decide things here, we look for what would have to happen for Judson to spend the night and if enough of those, no, all of those happen then we know that he is spending the night. We can start on either end. On the far end, we will know that he is spending the night if he comes back from your house in the morning. This is the kind of resolution that we can live with. It is the completion before the decision which is always better for the amount of pressure it takes off. Starting from the other end, we look at likeliest. It is likely that if he were to be spending the night there his toothbrush wouldn't be here. It is also likely that he would be sitting, at least for a little while in your car. It is also likely that he would be riding down the driveway in your car." It is amazing the way people think that they have to decide something before it comes about. What a sad life that results in. There really isn't any correlation between thinking and behaviors. You don't know this. Thinking can hone itself to the level of observation, learning to learn from what it really is doing rather than what it thinks it is doing. To pursue the truth you must become an observer, but if this were sufficient engineers would be happy. To pursue the truth you must beome a caring observer: an observer who cares past the point of comfort, past the point of personal preference and past the point of personal gain. You must be elected to a judgeship on which the other passengers spur you on to greater caring, objectivity and heights of sexual expansion.

If someone doesn't care it is because they don't have the attention span to care. If they don't have the attention span to care it is because they are sufficiently fearful that they commit to what comes into consciousness prior to its arrival on the "real" scene. If that is the case they will have no part of life that isn't regurgitated. And that is the way that fear and attention span are related, simply by deflating.

It would be complimentary immaturity to blame someone for having too short an attention span because the only reason that you would blame them is if you were engaged in the same pre-rinse cycle that they were, with different content of course, because they would be washing their dirty laundry and you would be washing yours.

It isn't as easy to have relating work as you think it is. If you think it is difficult it is even more difficult than that. If you don't think it is difficult it is way more difficult than that.

Somebody has to be more mature than somebody else and it certainly isn't going to be you. We may just have to redefine maturity to get the job done, better yet started.

Aside: I don't remember how much of what will come next I have already said in another chapter. I do know, that how ever much it was, the covering of it by me doesn't necessarily correlate with the covering of it in kind by you, so I reserve the right to be sufficiently interesting and far-out that I either repeat myself or not and don't know which and if you do know which I request that if I did repeat myself or if I didn't that you derive the most value from it that you can and if you want to let me know that you did do, and if you don't want to don't. How you read this book is up to you, how it is delivered to you is typically UPS and what you do with it is anybody's guess.

But I think it would help if you and I agree to a specific kind of relationship before we go any further. I want you to agree to be my lover or I just can't go on. No, not really can't go on, of course I can go on but it is unlikely to be the same. So, please be my lover, not for just now but forever. I promise unilaterally to be your lover. This won't entail tattoos but the correct spelling of my name is J-e-r-r-y, just in case.

There are all kinds of love in this world typically depending on the alleged direct object of your affections. There is the love you have for a dog, the love you have for a quartet, the love you have for the works of Beethoven, the love you have for your X, the love you have for your why, the love you have for your children's children, the love you have for Jesus, or similar metaphors, the love you have for baked beans, the love you have for your life and the love you have for me.[1] If I have a

---

[1] These different kinds of love are interchangeable. You can unplug one and plug the other one in. If you are too mad at your spouse you can plug in "dog love" taking some of the burden off your spouse. Once, on a walk with a mother, who was having terrible trauma with her two daughters, I suggested that she depose them to granddaughter status. That did the trick, she reduced her own burden and liked her kids again making her have more fun with them and also having them be more effective. On that same walk I came up with the idea, or game, called Query Reversal. In a Query Reversal, you find something you think is true and ask yourself questions, very pointed, questions about it until it reverses itself, moving from yes to no or from fact to fiction. As you get great at Query Reversals you will be able to shoot proverbial skeet before they become inflated, fat facts.

choice here I would prefer that you find a niche for our love somewhere between the love you have of your favorite pet ever, your deepest lover and a spiritual teacher beyond compare, like the best Eastern master ever. (If you missed that I just said it was beyond compare and then compared it you may want to start reading at a deeper level.)

Attention span and sample rate conspire to form an interface which saves you from having to interact directly with the general or specific public. These two are the secretary who won't let you through to the decision maker becoming the decision maker herself by deciding not to let you through.[2] Often I think the company would work more efficiently if you put the secretaries in the big offices and had the bosses answer the phones. But, still there you have attention span and sample rate. Attention span is how long, and how much, you can fit in the seven bits of attention before you have to shut down, clean up and start over again. Attention span is to lifespan what moments are to lifetimes. When your attention span shuts down, and it does very often, you integrate all it has in it with all that has gone before. Not so obviously you also integrate it with all that will go on ahead. When this integration is done, and it only takes tiny parts of seconds you get another unit of

---

[2] It is also your own secretary who decides she shouldn't let you through to your own office because you really aren't that much of a contribution to the company anyway. When the foot soldier becomes the general you will probably get your walking papers.

[3] The primary place attention span gets commented on, if not appreciated or lengthened, is in the school system. Children are perennially blamed for their lack of attention. It isn't really attention span that is the problem here, it is the teachers' inability to make a sale. One must continually design environments or relationships that inspire one to remain present until remaining present becomes so much fun that it perpetuates itself. Sufficient eccentricity enhances attention span and, I am told, strengthens the orbit and the risk at the same time which is enough to have one want to "find out what happens next."

attention to span. The wider the span the more you can bask in the connectedness of life.[3]

Attention span when lengthened makes one wiser, healthier and more intolerant of life wholly as a response and less likely to have one. When you come back from having checked out you are behind: you have to catch up. The dumbest way to do this is to try and carry something over, to make your surroundings so mundane that when you come back you fool yourself into thinking that you never left. This foolishness has you not know the difference between being checked out or checked in. With the loss of this difference comes the loss of nearly all other differences, you become a flat-lander and there is nothing like the long stretches of road in Nebraska and Kansas to inspire one to miss both exit and entrance and thus not enjoy the current state at all until one hits the mountains head-on. Not appreciating the great plains, of life, is a sort of philosophical dust bowl that prepares one to not enjoy the mountains by anything other than the cheapest of fixes: contrast. A head game that never gets you ahead. So, the way to lengthen attention is to span things that are more diverse. That way your span will be greater and you will reveal connections increasing the quality of your life both by lengthening span and making life interesting at the same time. The more diverse the points of your spin, the more energy they generate when played against each other and the more you get done in play without ever working. You get smarter and it takes no effort or specific learning to do so. The turbine in your mind spins, ahhhhhhhh, you have energy: a gain.

Sample rate is about the interaction between yourself and your context, or the context. Would you know ecstasy if it bit you? Or would you just report it to the animal control officer or local sheriff as a nuisance getting in the way of your everyday life? Nielsen, Gallup: these are sample takers. Sample rate is the rate at which you take samples of your specific internal or external environment and then generalize to the whole. Your sample rate determines, in part, how accurately, with your terribly finite consciousness, you can figure out your surroundings. Gallup, rides rapidly to conclusions, as he interviews a few select people to discover how a lot of people think. You process very little data, in relation to what is available on Earth, to discover the nature of Earth. You process very little data about a person to discover the nature of that person and then, with great wishful thinking, to determine your relationship with them. The more often you sample and the more diverse your sample, the more representative will be your conscious model of the whole.

Your quality of life is entirely dependent on knowing what is around you and being able to alternately extrapolate from what is around you what will be around you should you continue on the same course AND to create what is around you knowing that what you created bears little or no resemblance to what is really around you but somehow by its very creation makes your life both more fun to live and more inspirational for other fictional functuaries to join you in a kind of simulated bliss. The former makes you an accountant, the latter an artist. Somewhere in the mating of number crunching and creating from nothing is the truth. The truth must be made up each moment and then discovered in everything. Sampling more bares the odd burden of tying you to Earth and doing non-routine maintenance on the launch pad.

Lengthening attention span and increasing sample rate are the co-conspirators seeking the revolution that will put a "the truth" in every pot. With a chicken in every pot, people are just too scared but with the truth in every pot they are free, they think, if not in their thinking. Thinking thinks it's free when it is most like a broken record.

You can go about this pursuit on your own, and you have and you will. But you can also go on it with another. When you aren't alone you can kiss from time to time and that makes everything worthwhile. If you are brave enough you can touch too; you can touch their world and have your attention span and sample rate dominated with them. This is the definition of surrender and it is the shortest path to truth. Though it often doesn't seem to be the easiest, all others are much harder, each other is harder. Surrender is one of the few things that by its very nature doesn't get easier over time or people.[4]

If you are in relationship there is an implicit agreement for that other person to hold you. If you are not in relationship you are released from this unity on your own recognizance, which means you incarcerate yourself with whatever you think or think often enough to know. But, and this is a big but, if you are in relationship you should at least, at times, be free from carrying yourself. Free from carrying yourself, in a state which worships choice as thought and as though it exists, is highly underrated. Having somebody carry you should be part of the minimum daily requirement for a healthy life. But, when they have indicated contractually, marriage or work, or implicitly, family or friends that they will hold you and they don't, then you are in trouble: alone, with echoes to negotiate with. You don't hold yourself, they don't hold you; you fall through the cracks. It isn't that much fun to fall such. It isn't that much fun to fall at all. But, if you fall and there is someone around to blame for not catching you then you are really in trouble because you will not learn about yourself in the process of falling; instead focus your attention on her as you learn something that isn't really true about her. In other words: You die by

---

[4] I am drowning a distinction here between "truth" and "the truth." This is an important distinction and one so worth your time that any further explanation would be redundant.

degrees and end up doing relating without relating, which is holding yourself at night and during the day and not telling your loved one when your birthday is because you would rather give yourself the presents that you deserve instead of leaving it up to him.[5] And one of the reasons that this link in the "doesn't work" chain doesn't work is that if he gives you a present he may give you a present either worse than you think you deserve or better than you think you deserve which gives him the power to dashU or expandU. This is the power that in fact every human being on the planet has over you but nobody knows it. Relating to one person is a step along the upward path to relating to everybody. Yipes and Yipee.

All it takes in relating is one sideways step for you to confuse coincidence with cause and you will blame whoever it is for whatever it is while flushing the relating down the lovers lane toilet in the process. In other more simple words: If you have a bad day at work and get angry with your spouse for nothing when you get home you may think that getting rid of your spouse would help but more likely you will think that your spouse is to blame so you need to stay away from her or him so you work more hours. The nature of thinking is that it is slow. It is so slow that you get hurt and feel the pain enough later that by the time you are ready to figure out what hurt you it is well out of attention span and seems unrelated. You then blame something else and make decisions accordingly which gives, in each moment, something to be thankful for. That something to be thankful for is that you can't directly influence your behaviors with your thoughts. Please let go of the idea that you can, relieving, at the same time, your thoughts from any relevance beyond entertainment, and your behaviors from being judged.

---

[5] You even limit yourself to one birthday a year which is the stupidest thing I ever heard, unless you are allergic to birthdays in which case you have little to look forward to.

Wouldn't that be neat?

There are things that are easy to let go of and things that are much harder to let go of. The typical coefficient here is how closely one has held a certain something to the bosom. Bosomhood spawns the illusion of safety while demanding the armor of thinking as a mediator of sorts.[6][7][8]

Consciousness[9] is: Seldom defined but specifically definable. Part of the nature of defining is that it takes consciousness to do it theoretically. Practical definition is use. Theoretical is thinking in the absence of specific stimuli. Consciousness is the ability to make up a model in one's head that has, more or less, likeness

---

[6] Sorts refers here to the various very, but not varied, important patterns that people run in order to enhance and update the similarities or dissimilarities of things prior to releasing them on their own cognizance to consciousness. It is important to let go. It is vital to let go. But what does letting go mean? To find out, you have to go through the hollow following the tracks of your tears all the way to the islets of Langerhans, go forward about two inches and begin digesting the present at an alarming rate.

[7] To discover what it, really, means, we have to explore it without object so a brief tour of the sight of letting go would be useful. In other words: If you have models for letting go you should assemble them now and smash them to within an inch of your life. But, seriously, letting go requires some background, oddly the background is you. We have to discover not what you think you are but what you really are on the way to who you think you are. To do so we need to tease out, quickly, the main attribute that you have which makes you different than every other species on the planet: consciousness.

[8] Classification is an attempt to institutionalize useful distinctions in an attempt to save time while determining whether something is that particular something that you should mate with or not. The very act of institutionalizing field dresses usefulness, leaving nothing but entrails not worth following because the animal has already been dragged neither kicking nor screaming from the seen of the crime. I find classification two parts useful and two parts stifling so I suggest that you use it to expand when you can and contract when you must.

[9] Consciousness, too, is the withering away of brain function into mind function in the absence of attention to bodily function: dysfunctional.

to something that could or is already existent in the world. The greater the similarity to something already existent in the world, the stiller the life.[10]

Consciousness is seven (really someplace between five and nine) bits of data that are by their nature negotiable, transient, semi-salient and perfectly imaginary.[11] They are also self-defining, self-limiting and in their absence, self-expanding. Consciousness is anything that shows up in your head as a thought, meaning a composition of pictures, sounds and feelings without needing to be polished, maintained, polished off, consumed or mated with. Consciousness is not real but consciousness filling its bits with reality is spirituality. Consciousness is the ability to perceive what is not there or to not perceive what is there. It is not to be confused with sensory input, awareness, because it is no closer to sensory input than the maple leaves are to maple syrup. Yes, a very watered down version of maple syrup does show up at the site of manufacture, the leaves, but it is not sufficiently like it to be useful. Consciousness, too, is so watered down that it is related to but not useable by who you really are. The purpose of consciousness is entertainment though you wouldn't know that from watching how people use it. You would know it if you were having a good time but wouldn't know it if you were trying to control anything. If consciousness is entertained it is always closer to truth and reality than if it is not. It is when consciousness is camelliing under the burden of anything, that anything, held closely enough and tightly enough obscures both truth and reality.

---

[10] At one level, since objects themselves do not move from outside you to inside you for you to see them, and since the eyes are not limited or even related to the concept of windows, everything is made up in the mind. There are specific chemical and electrical, billable at the level of attention, exchanges which inspire the idea in one of a cat or a table, the proof of said cat or table depending, as always, on use.

[11] Decisions are bit debaits not resolved easily.

The real sample rate (remember sample rate?) we are interested in is sampling reality, the name of these samples is truth.

CHAPTER 17

Getting There—
Responsibility—
Your Marbles

You have three gatekeepers, two arms between them, one shorter the other longer, defining the order of things and wrapped around a non-negotiable dial in an attempt to have you concede. Your arms up behind your back but you still hear the ticking of your heart. You can't find yourself before the bomb goes off or can you?

Does anybody really know what time it is?[1] This is the human race, was that the starting gun, if so what the heck are you waiting for? I think I heard it and the penalty of a false start is always less than missing the start. The turtle wins by a hare. Speed is scary, speed is neat, it gets you out of jams and into them with the same non-caring alacrity.

Go, orientation, welcome to the past, present and future hall of fame. This is your great, great, great grandmother, this your children's children's kid sister. They meet, they talk but they don't really understand each other, any worse than you do

---

[1] Chicago, please listen now. Putting anything off in the face of anything else expresses you directionally in an unknown but immediately preferred direction.

your piers. Time isn't on your side, unless you use it to inspire yourself::[2] endlessly.

It seldom ceases to surprise me how past, present and future make people tense. The one they ignore in order to have a twosum, is always the present if for no other reason than that past and future are sufficiently opposed to distract long enough for the present to sneak through without being noticed. Watch what? Watch. As long as you have only these three you will be wrenched from a split world, from a world of dichotomies into a waltz-king world where you are nearly always negotiating with the little you and including to the exclusion of the big picture.

Cosmetic surgery just doesn't make sense after a certain age: undertaking such vanity isn't something you would do if you knew the clock was running out.

The cure for this timely madness isn't a matter of perspective but changing names. When you get married you may change your name and probably should. If you don't you've missed the opportunity to enter the union faceless, finding face.[3] Most people form a superficial union missing, this time the point. The whole point is to become the whole, a new, entirely new, entity that must be dealt with by creating a new context with new attention. Sure, you can learn from what you built before but any similarity between the new you and the old you is plagiarism and will be treated evolutionarily as such. That's a threat, but unlike evolution it is personal and provides a way out solution.

If there is to be a Santa Clause then what you get for

---

[2] Remember the TB test. If not please find someone who knows what this :: means when tattooed on your skin. *Hint:* They will be between forty five and sixty years of age and are very likely to be either younger or older than you.

[3] Alias, alas, only an I away.

Christmas has to, by definition, be out of your control.[4] Sure you can write a letter but you know nobody writes letters anymore and if nobody is writing them nobody is reading them. If you write letters to a fictitious person you aren't really clearing the water either.

So let's. Rather than starting with as little a thing as a letter, just a letter, and not yet getting up to a whole letter itself, just barge in and rename these three little monkeys. Hear no evil, speak no evil, see no evil won't work because it is precisely the censoring of the senses which got us to this impasse, amBush, where we needed such spice that we couldn't even taste our food anymore.[5] We have to go with something other than tasteless and something other than so tasteful. Subtlety and depth go together We have to go deeper, much deeper. We have to take something that seems not to make any difference on the surface, for if you disturb the surface your attention will naturally go to the surface. We have to alter the composition of things vertically, amounting to counting out content and reaching into ourselves past the "Do Not Disturb" sign, all the way down to the bottom of the well. Sure, you will get a bit nauseous falling such, but the surface just doesn't get you to mines. The good stuff, the valuable stuff, the truly shiny wonderful stuff about you is underground allowing you to piddle away a lifetime unless you go down. For once leave the horizontal alone, for once fall when you could have stood fast. This is easy, though not very common. All it takes is an inoculation against low self-esteem. This inoculation is a minuscule, homeopathic dose of you until you learn to, live off, finding yourself

---

[4] Why does Santa come earlier every year but never stay later? Does this mean Mrs. Clause is in charge of the workshop? I have heard the elves are afraid of Mrs. Claws.

[5] Advertising will get harsher to the point where it will cause even greater physical damage than it does already.

in your surroundings. In this case we will give you something to do until you can admit that you exist on your new terrain. The biggest problem with past, present and future is that they are sterile. They are the same for everybody and don't contain sufficient spin to carry on a world of your own, thus sticking you in a situation where any little imperfection seems permanent taking over all three without getting permission from any one. Nobody's home unless you find yourself there.[6]

Let me explain then, patient reader, then we will get on with the renaming: recently we were in a store and became captivated. Judson (Judson9@alltel.net) requested that we go to Smoky Mountain Knife Works on our way back from vacation. Judson has a penchant and passion for knives enough to last a lifetime. In this mammoth store there was a very big cauldron nearly full of marbles. These were, are, will be, like no other marbles I have seen. They were, are, will be, made of granite and many of them had little painted patterns on them. They looked old, the claim was 1900 or so, they were fun to look at, and seemed tough enough that they would never wear out. They got our attention, held our attention and we still like them. If you can think big think bigger; we bought roughly three thousand.

If you know why, what is the point? If you know what, there is something else you don't know. I had no idea what they really were or why I had 3,000 but soon found out. When we got home I put one of the marbles on our kitchen table. It didn't just sit there, it rolled. It moved very oddly back and forth, sideways, like a Mexican jumping bean.

---

[6] There are little identifiable and identifying pieces of you in everything. If you don't like yourself these are a constant threat, like mirrors to people who think they are ugly. If you do like yourself they will be like gourmet snacks that just don't count or run counter to your two-week fast.

It lengthened my attention span by giving me way more than I expected. It rolled around terribly unpredictably for maybe thirty seconds, then wobbling in almost one spot finally, thank God, stopped.

Aside: Did I mention that we bought a lot of these? If I still have these as you read this, which is likely I would be delighted to do a very odd thing, share them. If you are brave you can use the above e-mail address or this address and ask for one of these little granite cuties, if we still have some left, which is likely, and you tell us in 50 words or less why we ought to. Somebody around here we'll send one to you: they are cool. (Mail to: Attention: Hey You, PO Box 2422, Clarkesville, GA 30523)

A secret: Though each marble looks quite round it isn't that round. There are irregularities, imperfections in each which make each restless. I set another one down, a different marble, a different dance but still way more than I bargained for, this one set off on nothing like a straight path and found its way off the edge of the table. I watched and watched as these little things rolled in the best simulation of volition I have ever seen in an inanimate object. All I had to do was try and set it down and it wobbled around magnificently.[7]

---

[7] If you were to kick a stone and rather than just going maybe four feet and coming to rest, that stone ran on for thirty feet, did a little dance and moved all over the place you would do something very interesting: you would raise your attention. That stone, with its magic would get so much of your attention, revealing at that moment that you had a specific expectation, based on physics, that you didn't know you had but still had.

This physics assumption is kind of like a king or queen that dominates your life, limits your attention and restricts the kind of fun you can have on Earth. This unnoticed ruler only shows him or herself when you are surprised by something that should fit and doesn't. In the extreme, imagine that you have a ping-pong ball and that you let go of it but it doesn't drop. Remember the cartoons in which the creature runs off the cliff, pauses, notices that it has run off the cliff and then falls? That is funny and what is the particular kind

CHAPTER 17

So, the marble rolled around in an odd, drunken sort of way, then reached a particular digital imperfection where it rocked back and forth like some mental patients do, finally letting go of my massively increased attention by settling down like a hen on her nest. The first time this happened I got "wonder," the second time "mystery." The third time "humor," and the fourth time I just got, evangelism, having to call somebody over to watch it with me because I couldn't stand to see it one more time without a witness. As I write this it seems an exaggeration: it isn't. Typically you have to contract your definition of miracle to have it become consistent but not with these hard little jewels. Sure enough, it inspired the same things in my friendly new observer as it had in me. If you lengthen your attention span you increase your perception of connection, uniting your world and untying your tethers.

Maybe, and this really is true, it is our imperfections and irregularities that give rise to attention. Maybe, and this is really really true, it is the consistencies of life that put us to sleep and the oddities that give us more than we bargained for, showing us that when we gamble we really can get entirely unpredictable results making predicting not really all it is cracked up to be and returning us to the present. The marble taught me that.[8]

---

of funny about it is that your attention is created and focused very aggressively until the inevitable happens. You have, through the suspension of physics, discovered that something you thought wasn't possible is, and where you have held it, safe, that it wasn't possible. You have been forced to yield, effortlessly. A short-term operator is attention, the cost is limitation and the unpredictable payoff is humor, always.

[8] If you are sitting on the fence at the crack of dawn you may want to budget your time. Sure they tell you the odds, which seemingly reduces your risk, but it doesn't. If you lose you still lose all your money, odd these odds because the odds don't soften the blow but they do indicate a specific limit to the upside. The odds really don't tell you what it will take to get even again once you have slipped downward in your own opinion of what should have happened.

143

Then, I set a marble down while giving it a horizontal spin, like a top. The game was over. The spin, imparted, overrode the imperfection and there was no wobble, no too much movement to believe and the marble acted a little too much like Earth in predictability. My attention didn't rise, I didn't laugh and I didn't want to spread the word. Just the least little bit of spin and the game was over. Spin, the political term, is increasingly relevant in lowering our attention, thus getting in the way of our enjoyment of life. It has us be so busy with our preferences and what we think is there that we miss that every time we do anything or think anything the return on our investment is both more massive and of an ongoing, never-ending, eternal sort. Yes, we are already then, now and forever, whether we like it or not.

A round little piece of granite knows that, but we tend to forget anything that will set us free: our imperfections, insecurities and irregularities make us volatile, volitional and interesting. If you can celebrate it you are entertained by it. If you are entertained by it you and it win; your independence and loneliness are over possibly forever. Ye who are without sin cast the first marble. If you have lost your marbles we will send you one. Ye who are with sin cast the first marble.

One thing I will not forget is the subtle renaming which will reveal your imperfections sufficiently that you will be humored by them, want to see them and even be evangelical about the new you you meet through altering,, drastically, in a little way, your interface with attention/space: time.

[9] One of the many things we have discovered here but one of the more useful is that you make a lot of pictures in your head and that the number of those pictures which include you in them has a lot to do with your attention to yourself and too soon your self-image. If you lost yourself, which you have, you could find yourself again simply by having yourself appear in every picture in your head. *Voilá*, there you are, pretty soon you like yourself better, the pain in your psycho goes away and you just spread everywhere, making your thinking a cross between a virus and a parasite, which is how it really should be anyway.

The renaming is euphemistically as follows, sorry for the order: past=explanation, present=responsibility, and future=creativity.[9]

When you rename these three, this simple little shift allows you to put yourself in them. It lets you know a useful interface by which you can exist beautifully across time lines and move more freely, a time traveling. Obviously this takes care of your interactions with everything that you don't yet perceive yourself to be or not to be. That is the answer and incidentally also takes care of death.[10] If you could get this much from just a name change you would be changing your name all the time, and you should and you can. The moment that someone recognizes you it is time to change your name. The ascension of aliases here is enough to make life beyond interesting all the way from defensive to creative with an endless stop in the present. In other words: When you are set down somewhere you should be able to inspire wonder, mystery and evangelism in your surroundings, and you do. You don't notice that you do, so you try and do something which will produce what is already there: a spiral of discontent in a sea of perfection. You can only pull this trick off when you are well and truly blind to who you really are. This feat is accomplished by trying to gloss over your imperfections and irregularities and getting mad, or superior, when you see them in others.

When your environment defines your adjustment rather than you doing so, increasing your interactions with said

---

[10] Breaking news: If you wrap death in yes it becomes not only palatable but inspirational. If you meet death with any no at all it becomes sickening and feebling. Maybe, and I think this is likely, death has no nature of its own. Maybe, and I think this is even more likely, there is no thing that has a nature of its own and it is human nature which gets snuck into them, vaulting them into our attention on a firstly horizontal then vertical pole that makes spreading our life around so standard as to be invisible. If we caught ourselves, thus vaulting, we would never have to respond again, discovering that we really only respond to ourselves.

environment to the point that you create a time in which you dominate your environment by using the very heart of physics to demand an increase in attention sufficient to produce a new species for old while pretending that nothing has happened, you get terminally busy doing nothing of lasting value. "He or she who finished last is the hardest worker" mentality.[11]

Explanation comes in two flavors, both of which only have to do with stories (please remember that we are talking about the past here). All explanations are stories, representatives of things, diplomats that set up a false front since the real front would be too expensive and have a back and inside that wouldn't really be used in the shallow first impression sufficient to cause a reaction. An explanation is a story. It is not the thing itself, but it often passes truth detectors with sufficient false nose and glasses to pass for something it is not making one, at best, an anachronism and at worst a curmudgeon. With an explanation you can justify or you can entertain. A justification is a title fight between how and what. How you perceive yourself to be taking on what you really are. How usually wins by editing, by guile, by deletion. The most audacious critic is the one who doesn't look at all, the most con vincing one is the one who looks but only sees partially and the revolutionary one is the one who sees so much that others can't guess what the subject of the criticism is. Most of what you say is an argument that nobody wants to hear about something that isn't true and it boils down to one statement, "This is why I am good."

Remember, if you are mounting a defense your attention is already taken relegating you to thought of the past and future. The second kind of story is for entertainment. These delightful little beauties increase both humor and attention by discovering that two things are connected that you didn't know were

---

[11] Last time I asked my wife, I am no longer married, to take out the garbage she sought the protection of the thirteenth amendment (slavery).

connected. Entertainment is entertaining. It makes you happier and, not so obviously, smarter too. Justification always makes you less happy and dumber. Entertainment boils down roughly to the statement, "This is why things are even peachier." I could go on about stories for a long time but won't because when I was a very young child and was fishing with my platinum-haired grand, really, father he looked over at me and said, "The fish are in the shallow, in the deep or inbetween, but, they aren't in the boat, we are, and if they were we would probably be in the drink and they would be holding poles and we would be getting hooked (aren't we?)." The moral of his story, born out by results, is that the fewer fish we caught, the more likely we were to keep our prized, if perpetually hungry, position of being high and dry and watching the sunset on another fishless fishing expedition. If we caught fish then we would think there was some correlation between fishing and catching fish, having our fun fishing be dependent on a lesser species that by the very act of not being caught seemed greater than us, inspiring in us a questioning of the value of the whole human race which, since we weren't ever catching anything, we had the time to ponder any way we wanted. We did, and my grandfather was grand and we had leftovers for dinner and they were delicious and I urge you not to worry about me, really. Why, because I love you and anyone who loves you is OK in my book.

Suffice it to say that you have to find out what in your life, both spoken out loud and repeated echoing reality in your head is stories,, and then you have to explore whether with this one, this particular story, you are justifying or entertaining remembering, all the while, because otherwise you leave time to an objective limbo which has you define important with busy and worthless with nothing, setting you up to a black-and-white-do-matter and grey-doesn't-matter-at-all, so you have to wonder why you got a brain in the first place but you don't have time to wonder such things, so you plod on breaking old ground for new crops. But, entertainment can solve all this, and a name change is entertaining, or can be, and you don't ever have to be busy. By the power of the written word vested in me I give you the next ten years off and your vacation really begins when you,,,, not under duress, because anything done under duress, which is almost everything, doesn't count, admit that you are a philosopher and that you are living out of your philosophy.

Remember if you are justifying you are defending an imaginary castle against an imaginary siege and such things seldom end, and if they do, never end well.

The third beast, under the stories, that I didn't warn you about, and the first one not of burden, is responsibility. Responsibility brings you to the present by having you admit the imaginary causal link that passes for causal, connection, in a world with ownership supplanting being as the highest form of interaction, between you and anything that is well on the way to being you. If you give the other team the football because you don't know what to do with it, and because you have a good defense, you put a whole new complexion on the game. Responsibility is admitting that it is by your response that things will get either better or worse but really are the way they are now. Responsibility is the presence of flexibility this moment. Responsibility boils down to "because I said so this will be." It is the end of explanation and the birth of actuality out of possibility. Responsibility is an opportunity, unless it slips a little past, and then it is blame. It is impossible to estimate the number of human lives that have been ruined by this little bit of past eking through. Responsibility is the creation of a place-holder keeping the connection between you and something open until the real connection reveals itself. It is a foothold, a handhold but never a mind hold. It is physical not mental. Responsibility is the sharp blade that easily cuts out a place large enough for you to exist or whittles nearly anything into the shape of anything else without any ulterior motive at all. Responsibility frees while appearing not to. God has complete responsibility for everything, setting God free to do anything, or, nothing. You have a set amount and when that set point advances you have more attention and more identification, in the best way, with all the other who you ares. You discover that the place you thought wasn't friendly, is. You discover allies in high, low and medium places. There is a specific relationship between responsibility and maturity that doesn't really have to be the case but is enough of the time that I thought I better warn you about it.

Creativity is your interface with the future. It boils down to "Ha." If you can catch what will be while it is still what could be,, you can, without control, nurture all facets of something that isn't in such a way that when it becomes what is you are the best kind of mommy and daddy to it. Here is your chance to make your bed while not lying about it, in it or near it. What if you could buy, for a limited time, a self-making bed so that anytime you thought about making the bed it just made itself? This wouldn't preclude lying in it but it could save a lot of time especially if you take my advice and take a lot of naps. There is a place before possibility which is called spirituality. From spirituality something like quantum foam moves to possibility. Possibility is the greatest expanse not known but knowable by personkind. Possibility flows from just anything to probability and then to actuality. This is a subject best taken care of on its own though and it deserves its own chapter which, if I have any ability to influence things at all, will be the next chapter.

CHAPTER 1 8

Death:
Almost Being

It is tempting to study what is. If you do so you miss be coming. If you miss be coming your latitude of play will be so severely restricted that you won't notice but you will suffer the consequences which are usually being backed into a corner of reaction. You will be like a wolverine who wanders out of the wilds into downtown New York. Not maybe exactly like that but a little. In the wilds a wolverine is pound for dreadful pounding the toughest animal in the world. On the domestic scene it can't hold a candle to any wronged party in a relationship.

If we are going to study what isn't, yet, there are many points at which it isn't as it nears "is." It wanders along a line of isn't quite undisturbed by existential issues, bless you. Its wandering is interrupted by one of two things, depending on where you come down on the tree in the forest and the horrible noise it seems to have made for so many years: 1) If a human notices the possibility of the event happening in advance of the event happening then the event has inspired attention prior to existence, setting up attention, created from nothing. Attention prior to existence is attention from and on nothing. This is consciousness before life.[1] Blowing this out is a graphical

---

[1] Heidegger deserves a little credit for his "already listening" or how to be here not now.

event in which we explore the correlation of the first noticing of the possibility of the event and the event, in fact, happening. It will move through different stages from its first appearance on the radar screen as a possibility, near zero probability, to one hundred percent likelihood: actuality. Somewhere near the middle is about fifty percent likely (see Graph A). 2) If it doesn't get noticed prior to its happening then the only possible human interaction with it is response. The terrain between possible and actual is the only human playground where one can have input on the shape and type of playground. Anything less is interacting with somebody else's idea of monkey bars, swing or slide. Being a response is almost typical, being a stimulus, (1. which results from nothing, is semi-blessed. This is because of the near inability of human beings, given their insecurity, to distinguish between the words stimulus and cause. Cause is the inanimate reflection of the word stimulus. Or, stimulus is the only living descendent of cause, though its lack of lineage is never in doubt. In other words: Stimulus is to animate what cause is to inanimate. Or, stimulus plus perspective equals cause. When you move, always unnoticed, from stimulus to cause you lose your life, livelihood and preferred limb in the process. There should at least be some kind of a funeral for such an event. But, there usually isn't which has (2. you slide into three (3. not noticing.[2]

If you can think that something is possible and not be threatened by its lack of existence, or threat of existence, you

---

[2] There are more possible confusions here than meet the body, the eye or the mind. There is the possible confusion of cause with stimulus, there is the possible confusion of stimulus with response, there is the possible confusion of cause with effect and the possible confusion of stimulus with effect. Crossing the boundaries of animate to inanimate is like death and resurrection déjà vu style. You just have to be able to tell the difference between something that is alive and something that is not because without doing so you can't really explore the preponderance of options available to life or the consistency death provides as an incentive to live.

can enjoy the ride. If you can't, every ride is to the gallows with your focus on the end. Focus on the end is reaction, focus on what isn't gives birth to stimulus. If you can be a stimulus please do, but doing itself puts you behind the 8 ball again. So if you can be a stimulus please don't do, don't even be, just stimulate before it is too late.

You wouldn't want to drive a roller coaster, the designer drives it by the design. One of the main points of a roller coaster is that you are along for the ride, not along for the drive. There you are at Six Flags, hands on the wheel, feet where the brakes should be. You have to steer or die, it's the stuff of an adventure movie. The ride would be very different because you could mess it up. People love to be in control but at the first sign of trouble they are usually willing to admit, at least legally, that they are not. Who cut down that tree in the forest and did he or she wear protective ear gear?

The essence of roller coasters is that you are along for the ride, the essence of life is that you are along for the ride. Who designed this thing after all? You become a name dropper, "When I was at God's house the other day...."

Life gets difficult when you think you are the driver. Most people have white knuckles and worn-out muscles from trying to steer and control when neither is possible. It is time to actively enjoy the ride. Observation is the key to having the option to think you are driving or not. It is a sort of subtle? driver's? license granted by Heisenberg to go any speed you wish. The, often-not-so-sheer but shearing, speed limits of others are born, a heavy load can make it not worth the journey which leaves you thinking that you are missing something. If you made the journey and got to grandmother's house you would, I hope, find out quickly that the very nature of grandma's exis-tence is her big "no's," as in: "Grandma, what a big nose you have." Without observation you aren't stuck but it sure seems like you are, having your seems possibly burst from the real impacts in the imagined world.

The sooner you can notice anything the better, especially if it isn't there. If you notice it by its existence you are too late. The sooner you notice, before it is, the greater the temptation to try and mess with it, or control it. Readiness correlates with early detection, the earlier the better. If you put on the prophylactic after you have had sex it just doesn't do any good. If you open up you may get sick but if you then close up you will get sick. Closing is locking the fox in with the hens because you just can't tell which is which, again.

Arriving early won't make you ready for IT but it can give you time to find you: do your hair, your lips and work your way down. "I'm a wreck just now." is a quote often attributed to the Edmund Fitzgerald. "Too late?" We have a cutting board made from wood extracted from the bottom of Lake Superior. How far, how deep do you have to go to find a virgin? In this case it was under maybe a hundred feet of freezing cold water. Everybody is a virgin at some level. You get to find that level and you can pick a perfect bouquet.

When you find a virgin his or her virginity resonates with yours. Righteous indignation is only allowed from virginity, though it tends to consume it so imbibe, at your own risk, in what isn't prior to your parents coming home.

The sooner you notice anything the more existence that possible event lends to you.[3] Thus the more existence you have. You saw it before it existed, you get to be there for the birth. It isn't an accident that people consider the moment of birth to be a sacred moment. If you notice it soon enough and observe it through all the stages without getting hooked you get to be a midwife to life. The baby may die, not happen, or it may die,

---

[3] Becoming is a lending library, existence can be shared when caught early enough.

happen, but none of this goes on your permanent record because there is only one permanent record.

There you are at the Statue of Liberty, in France and there you are at the Louvre while they were building it. There you are talking with Leonardo as he is picking out ceiling paint. All these photos make your existence no longer in doubt but in curiosity. From doubt you will seek resolution, from curiosity you will be on relatively variable vacation even if you still have to go in to work.

If attention hasn't noticed that it has happened prior to its happening then it will begin to notice once it has happened. Too late even for paint-by-number or TV dinner. No artistic or gourmet experiences here (see Graph 2). A still life is no way to live though it may look real. You are still born, but not stillborn; the former meaning each moment, the latter meaning dead. The two are as different as they can get and seem the same.

The only way to act justifiably and semi-appropriately in relation to something is once it is perceived as being there completely. This dawning in the door of prior existence is a bit like trying to have sex with the new mother to influence the hair color of the first born. Never trust a bleached blonde, she really is something else. The sort of oblivion that results from being oblivious or obvious to existence is at best the lack of existence of the observer and at worst the loss of credibility of the witness, or the desire to watch team sports on TV and then brag to your friends that you did and then having them say, "Of course, me too." Remember, "Me two." is a schizophrenic's anthem.

There is a correlation between arriving too late, after birth, and suffering. Suffering is always a response and responses are only possible too late.[4] The essence of suffering is some degree of: "There wasn't anything I could do about it. Really." If, at that point you look at them not believing, tilt your head a little and say, "Really?" they will always get upset: at you? That is because they know, at some too virginal level, that they could have arrived earlier, in fact did, but won't admit it even under the duress they call life.[5]

When you don't know what isn't you have the luxury of seeking. When you don't know what is you can only react, never meeting the muse but claiming, loudly and automatically, that you do regularly. Sometimes it is best not to hire yourself as a guide. The scouts may be expendable but they are also the most interesting people to hang around.

If you live with your arms open you will embrace what is and what isn't. If you open them when something seems worth hugging you will miss a lot of hugs and never end up hugging nothing. Hugging nothing is tantamount to hugging yourself which is a pretty neat activity to engage in until something else comes along. If you live with your eyes open you will hug at the speed of light: observation.

When actual is greeted with open arms attention has been playing with possibility or faith and either way stuck isn't stuck anymore because that was seen on the way in too. To be, present at the birth of attention, is to be present at the birth of man; to do this presence you need more than just your arms open. You get to have everything open.

Embrace illusion and reality, knowing which. Embrace everything, your intellect will seem worthless, your rationality

---

[4] Responding very early to what isn't has you either be an incredible artist, for it is the roots of art, or the wholly forgotten son of God. If Paul Revere had arrived two months earlier or two months later his name wouldn't be appropriate, he wouldn't even be remembered.

[5] If you get caught under the dress you get caught under the influence. You never meant for it to get this far because there is no meaning. You just went there because it was there. Not so obviously you went there because you were here, laying siege and having little babies long before you thought they were due. Each thought is a child, though many of them appear to be bastards.

will scream "no," in an anti-seduction attempt but out of this you will be able to celebrate possibles instead of being stuck with actuals. I never was too inspired by actuarial tables though I have only snacked at them when I was alone at night, curled up wishing I wasn't thinking of death.

When you mountain climb with possibles instead of actuals you don't need a very big mountain. You can generate fear equally at the front or back step. You can have anything without leaving how and without leaving home without it. Then, and only then leaving home becomes an exaggeration of life, increasing only slightly possibles because it is only a limitation of the perception of possibles that makes life not worth living but only reacting. Welcome to the Biggest Show on Earth: all you have to do is get there before the show starts. Once the show has begun it is terminal, it will go through to the ends as a tribute to the unfounding fathers. Existence forces response, pre-existence beckons inviting attention. Would you rather have your arm forced up behind your back or get massaged. Would you rather react to the truth or be present at its birth.[6]

Possibles reach beyond existential proportions, the perception of one can be greater than the sum of all parts. This is the great economy of attention. (See my book *Economics of Attention* for more on this.) If the holographic nature I have just described isn't a deep enough payoff for you, attending earlier also allows you to avoid death.[7] If you show up early enough, attend the possibles party, you can remove attention from the event just post-existence and enjoy the nearly instan-

---

[6] Sorry for the lack of question marks on these sentences. I do mean them as real questions but mean them as such important questions that that squiggly mark didn't dignify them as the complete inspiring thoughts that these questions are.

[7] If that too isn't enough payoff you will get laid a lot more often and know it.

taneous re-celebration of the next growth of possibility through probability to reality. The moment of birth of anything is also the invisible stimulus for the birth of attention. If there is enough attention to go around then what goes around has already come around and we have arrived which means that there is nothing to do but celebrate. This celebration being the free movement of attention, thus a life without barriers and with no preference for actual existence or perceived existence or pre-existence. You become ambitimetress, ambispacetress and ambiomnipotent. Omnipotence is the highest cure to impotency and it is only attainable through broadband seduction, with a lack of specific techniques. Death dies unexpectedly, with you as the willing witness. Nothing leaves without your perception if not your permission. Life can really be life if neither death nor anything else can sneak up on it. This is the end of death as we don't know it and the celebration of consciousness set free from lower brain functions and free to cover the ground between what isn't and what is. Without this freedom of creation there is no freedom at all.[8] Love, Pax.

---

[8] You have to be the midwife to attention just prior to being the midwife to life. Being the midwife to life is being the stimulus instead of the response. Being the midwife to attention is being there independent of being.

CHAPTER 19

The Borders of Spirituality

You are never too old for leapfrog. In this particular game it is between sex and spirituality with seduction as the process. You should be coming to, too, and leaving this world as ultimate preparation for this world and others. Either everything is preparation or nothing is. You are always almost going on a trip, at the edge of vacation and the edge of work.

After a couple "gins" Eli Whitney would admit his love for cotton. If you are under the influence of anything, like your own inventions, less than coming or going, life and death, you are thinking too much or too little of yourself. Too much, too lowly or highly, or too little, too lowly or highly. Imbalances like these begin with a rash rash of disrespect and end with an outbreak of dissatisfaction.

The philosophical "What is it all for?" doesn't cut anything here, nor does, an arbitrary, unearned, phony "dark night of the soul." Though you may be able to scare other trick or treaters, the strictly trickers or the strictly treaters will see right through you avoiding, dangerously, at universal peril of batback, the kind of radar like feedback that bats and people have, allowing them to navigate in the dark, one better than the other. In the case of bats it is out and back only so far. In the case of people it is the same, but can be much spiritually improved. It can be a batback from you all the way to the other side with data which can't be found here. This is the journey that, in short, doses are intuition, longer doses revelation, in much longer doses (minutes) enlightenment. The bat just gets meal or appeal.[1]

There is a fundamental spiritual miscalculation which plagues all legitimate upsides—that is how much data an intuition or revelation contain. They seem so short to us, they are like aliens traveling so fast with so much that the normal channels won't suffice. All we can do is rejoice or suffer in the awake of their wake. Thinking too slowly makes too much a no-wake zone. The deeper you go the less wake creates a superficial disturbance and the more intimate the disturbance becomes. I have heard one fish can feel the impression of another in the water three miles away. The tail swishes and the other tale responds: would that we weren't connected such.[2]

Though sound travels more slowly in water than it does on land it leaves more of an impression. It is much more difficult to swim a mile than to walk a mile. The medium for us on Earth is air: we burn it, cook with it, walk through it as though it isn't there, pollute it, purify it, dance with it, ignore it and live on it. It is no accident that travel through air is so easy. It is also no accident that we don't realize we are being effected as severely in air as in water or other more medium mediums. The willing-ness of air to leave no obvious impression is a call to subtlety that should not be ignored. Water, simplifying is H_2O, while air is O_2. The absence of hydrogen doesn't justify this difference,

---

[1] Pre tending the dark side while still on this, the light side, is always too shallow to really learn from. You have to take readings on the other side of death to get really interesting data while here. To do this you have to have taken sufficient readings here, observation, without moving on them.

[2] Removing our sanction,, attention, focus of consciousness, is tantamount in our own mind to calling off the event but it still goes on as scheduled just without us. This happens after death but when it happens during life, it is tragic unless, and this is the worst solution for tragedy, it happens so often it becomes the status quo. It doesn't count as a moment shared with someone or life if it is an *Oprah* moment.

and like thieves in the night we are not to take advantage of it either. We are to act as though everything we do is permanent, not like it can be blown away in the next tender breeze. We are to be the sales which catch the wind that move the sails that propel us to spirituality. Until we can derive permanence from transience, setting up a spiritoelectric generator, we will not be able to lift ourselves by our own bootstraps; and though any fool knows that isn't possible, any wise man knows that it is worth taking a very deep breath indeed and trying.

How is your relationship? I love you. Not because you are you but because I have no choice. In the absence of choice, love or something always shows up. The showing up is non-elective, what shows up is too. I have been instructed to love you from the other side, thus the worst you can do is ignore it, the best bask in it. It is, already existent, actual among possibles. Love has a "real" existence on the other side giving it an imagined, choice, one on this side but making it more real than anything else here. The impending opposite always says that and those who have glimpsed enlightenment obey first and notice afterward. They don't obey things of this Earth, though, for that is just a matter of convenience for those who don't yet see.

If you die in Death Valley you won't have anything to worry about in life any more. While this is sort of my point, it is, I understand with great duress, not understandable without it. If you live on the other side you die on this side. If you die on the other side you have the possibility of living on this side. Anything living on the other side remains ever-possible on this side but ever-actual on the other. I know, and it may help if you know, that we are dis cussing the border between life and death and what lies on this side and what truths on the other. Just because this subject isn't likely or comfortable it doesn't mean that you have to ignore it or cuss about it. Hell, we can just talk

160

about it the best we can and the best we can't at the same time maybe learning about our "real" limitations in the process. "Real" limitations are assets, imagined limitations are real liabilities.

There are two and only, maybe, two possibilities, I will find the third, if there is one, before you do. That is the nature of literature. There is General Reverence and Specific Reverence.

General Reverence, though logically in command is the least useful, though by its generalization it seems to be faster. It is really much slower. It results from one moment with your eyes open covering hundreds of moments with them closed. The ratio should be nearly one to one while you are on Earth, and for off-Earth betting, it can be almost anything. For the nearly one to one, dependent on your continued holding on an imaginary image of yourself, you need Specific Reverence. Specific Reverence is listening to the reverence in what is said rather than what is said. This is one of the highest gifts of process. When you listen to the reverence in what is said you naturally inspire a reverence for yourself in the process. This is done by applying what you have not yet heard but will hear, and trusting yourself to hear it, by mapping it to your life, specific and general, without editing it.

General Reverance, the Peter Principle ruler on low, is determining what you revere first rather than reading what is there and then spreading this reverence without thought or attention by specific criteria to environs based on one or several parameters such as proximity, duration, intensity, tempo or frequency. General Reverance always results in becoming a follower, being stupid and behind something you consider to be more than you are. Specific Reverence is "good" science.

When I was in college, Chuck and I did a little statistically significant psychological study. We placed posters of the alphabet all around a classroom of children young enough to be ours (yet not know the alphabet or have appreciation for what it can do and how it can symbolize love and life away). After two months we measured the kids' ability to learn the alphabet with that of a group of kids who had not been victims of exposure, oddly called the "control" group.[3] There are many variables here, I request that you temporarily respect me enough to apply, for brevity's sake and my attention span and the way my fingers are wearing away, General Reverence Theory accepting that we took care of the variables. Remember, I am writing the book.

The findings were as follows: The children who were exposed to the alphabet in a classroom situation with posters had a significantly harder time learning the alphabet than those who did not.

That just goes to show you.

Now I request that you move back to Specific Reverence and explore the possible repercussions of prior most likely unconscious exposure to the contamination that we call exterior design. I also suggest that you may want to consider whether anyone is really a virgin in a culture this loud. In other words: There are too few people and too many stimuli on Earth so the only way we can get a grip on this is to move elsewhere. It seems that there is nowhere material that is preferable to here so we have to move non-materially, transcending the pleasures of Earth to the much greater obtuse pleasures of the homeopathic angelic existence of   . There is no word on this plane for what I wanted to say there. On a plane you aren't aloud to say the word "bomb." I don't know if you are allowed to read it, but here you are not allowed to say or even think the word above without being thrust into a spiritual world which is

---

[3] Isn't it odd that the "control" group is the one in which we don't know what happened but we know that something specific, what we are measuring, didn't, so they are somehow in control of what we don't know? Science?

so much superior to this one that it contains this one fully and much more but no Simon and Carbuncle.[4]

The net clean-up result of enough people moving, for enough time, or given the shortness of breadth, breath and the experience often enough, to the spiritual world, is to leave a limited number of campers and carpetbaggers on Earth which has the unpredictable effect of motivating those who are left with the abundance of stimuli that they reduce the daily minimum numbness from too many toward so many less that peace ensues. Then, when you get back to Earth after your meditation, lifetime or R and R you will be peacefully surprised at all the pleasantness which threatens to lynch any idea you have of ever leaving again because it is so perfect here. In other words: Earth is the vacation spot from the real work of the spiritual world. If you ever, ever, ever, do anything here that you don't want to, you, at least in your own mind, ruin the vacation.[5]

There are no successful corporal solutions to corporal problems. There are only corporal solutions to spiritual problems and spiritual solutions to corporal problems. It is only by gracing the

---

[4] Moving to the spiritual world is not that different and no better than vomiting forever. I don't mean to threaten you here but just to let you know that should you think everything will work out over there I have to warn you, it is my duty, that it already has worked out and while that looks a lot like lack of choice, thus lack of power and control, you will have no luck if you try and influence, even within yourself, how it looks. I am telling the control junkies among you that there is no product there.

[5] Robots just want to not be robots so it is simple to plant in their programming the "fact" that they are not. You are on Earth but somebody forgot to put in your programming that this is really just a brief vacation in the real work of your life and death. While this may have been an oversight it doesn't end up looking like one because the result is dichotomies. If you were forced to play here, always, play would all become work. Since you don't have to play here, you can have work or play, having how you spent your life vacation really be an indication of your evolution, having play be the greatest test of advancement or retardation there is. Have a ball, play with it too.

apparent void between life and death that we can clean this place up and become the prayer instead of the prey.

Do you like apples?

How do you like them apples?

What was missed early on is that picking one apple, no matter what you do with it, doesn't really spoil the whole tree, or Earth. There are many more apples, some ripe, some overripe and some yet green. These are your apples, this is your orchard, you just need to sin a bit more so that you can really be clear on why you don't want to. "Ye without sin, get sinning." That is a corporal solution to a corporal problem and about as logical as "going for all the gusto."

A spiritual solution always contains so much more data that it can't mess up. A corporal solution always contains so little that its solutions contain more problems than answers. Example: If you meditate in a specific position, say cross armed, you may be called back from a dialogue with God by a cramp in your arm. This is a corporal solution to a spiritual problem. A solution cross veil is always this simple, this complete, this obvious and this unappreciated. A spiritual solution to a corporal problem is to give your money away to get rich. Though it doesn't make sense it does get, in a big way, to the essence of money. The binding of logic is breaking and the pages are all getting laid by the congressmen. It is time to clean up our act here on Earth with spiritual means, and it is time to take the worst of Earth and shoot it off into the spiritual world.

Spirit is the focus of consciousness on reality. Life on Earth is the focus of consciousness on illusion. Spirituality is the manifestation of reality in a specific location.

CHAPTER 20

A Bind: Revealed

If you sneak around at night filling up the eighteen holes and
dispensing with the flags you will have presented a deeper game
to any golfers, early birds, who will, should they be flexible
enough, discover that billiard golf is much more interesting than
regular golf. There is no doubt when you get the ball in the whole
but in billiard golf it is a matter of where your ball goes, what it
hits, what it misses and the score-keeping is always a matter of
attention. If your attention flags your score goes down because you
don't notice the connection of things. But the bind is that in
regular golf you only have to pay particular attention in proximity to the hole, which means that when you begin to play you
may yell "fore" but don't yell "foreplay" because the green is a destination not a means to an end. If you go for the green you may get
rich, and you may be able to prove, on paper, that you won but you
really won't, because the "realest" game on Earth is the perception
of connection and no matter how much you protest that you win
you know you didn't if you don't learn the lay of the land because
your next trip to the course will be no better than the least,, fewest
strokes, performing below par, one since you really only go for the
symbolic score rather than the deeper connections.

If a plumber plumbed this way none of your pipes would be
straight and water would always be running some degree of
uphill or downhill putting pressure perpetually on you.

Or, in the fabric, compared to many other strands of humanity, you will be odd or even. Buy yourself you will be degrees of odd or even too. There must be a balance between the group presence and individual presence otherwise you will be afraid to go to a party or unable to stay home alone, or unable to not stay home alone or afraid not to go to the party. Schizophrenia is the least that ensues when your solo and group don't match. You will tease out two uues, neither one of which has enough accuracy to serve as kindling in a pinch. You are almost always in a pinch of somekind, a pinch is a specific bind as opposed to a bind which is more general and a lifetime which is even more general, especially if it doesn't work well.

Emily and Judson play well, often, but the introduction of a third person into the die namic ends the fun for at least two. When there are more than five people the new, now old, math takes over and you are forced to group people together in sets. Your inability to make individual distinctions, wanting to run from yourself and not for office, has you not wanting to judge others, thus when it gets to forming groups the criteria used is insufficient to be useful and tracking toward fear and terror. You build a group you wouldn't want to join or wouldn't want to be left out of depending on whether you lean more toward being in a group or left out. You don't know what you are doing and the very nature of groups means this is the worst possible situation which is that there are other people around to watch you not knowing but pretending that you do as Shepherd ewe leads at least your own virtual flock to slaughter. What we need is more individual distinctions in the face of detonating the population explosion as we get rid of set theory, converting it to get set theory and finally to go theory. Which is one of the reasons that the Statue of Liberty looks on without blinking and the statue representing justice is blind. You get them here and then teach them how things work. The woman with the scales is blindfolded so that she will do the weighing without weighing preferences, since they don't really weigh anything anyway. You will have to learn to be personally partial before going to the party and you will have to learn to be impartial before going home alone.[1]

Or, no matter how nice your pants look if they bind in the crotch you will sooner or later wish that you were dead.[2][3] It is like this: You have been taught that you have control over your behaviors: you have been taught wrong. Since you think that you do you continually perform head butts to anything and anyone, especially yourself. You beat yourself up, spinning in place by the very nature of thinking, imagining that you can control something that you can't. This is enough, intentionally placed, to stop you from entering the spiritual world. You can't go spiritual until your corporal life works.

I used to get calls often, when I talked on the phone, from people who wanted to know about teleportation, astral travel and the like. As Werner Erhard said, "We need more mass

---

[1] When sociology becomes math it is finally useful as long as its constituents are treated as individuals. Psychologists are the secretaries of all states. Psychiatrists, especially Freudian or undersexed, are dick taters. If after sex, he or she is still there that is a bonus, at least, it better be. Standing up all night isn't easy and if you have to defend a one-night stand it isn't worth it.

[2] The extrapolation of overlooking discomfort is death with great pain slowing but not stopping your decent. Or. The parental owl longs for venting of bowel. The Ten Commandments were supposed to take care of this for people, so they didn't have to talk so much, but there is too much don't in them. Yes, a Bible based on no won't let you go forward but will have you walk backwards, mind-knotted.

[3] I figure that at chapter 20 my footnotes can be a little more obtuse as I have more to put and less of a shot at putting it somewhere. The footnotes will all still be deep and connected but not so obviously so. Like where would you put the following: Yul Brenner's head said, "You can't get hair from here?" I couldn't leave it out. I just wasn't about taking the time to find out that there wasn't really any place to nestle a stand alone quote.

transit before we can focus on teleportation." These people wanted to play with spiritual toys too early. If it is time for such toys you won't need to ask. You won't need to read and you won't need to buy this special crystal or that meditation pillow. "How is your family?" I would ask. It became obvious very quickly that their lives sucked and you can't get into Heaven while still nursing; the people around them were in bad shape and teleportation was some sort of escape from the malicious mundane mess they had manufactured by their neglect and laziness. Neglect and laziness won't get you into bliss, which is the launching pad for Heaven. It won't wake you up and it won't let you release what you are holding on to. You just can't track things into Heaven, you can't carry any lint in your belly-button on the way in and you can't get in with anything you don't want to look at or don't let go of here on Earth. You can't go yet and if you could go, meaning if you had cleaned everything up and had a perfect life, you wouldn't want to go.

You can tell everything by the condition of the people around you.[4] In fact, you may as well consider that you don't get to go until everyone around you votes that you must stay, maybe because they love you so much, but not because they can't do without you, they would have to do better without you and they don't want that. Here you need to determine how others see you, as a "Stop" sign or an indication to go? Their complete love is an invitation to transcendence, anything less is a paralytic pass on life.

So, the man doesn't want the woman to have an affair. We can want that, but what he wants has nothing to do with what

---

[4] It isn't easy but you have to be willing and looking at the people around you to find out exactly how you are doing. Hopefully, if the people around you are doing well they will be looking at you to find out how they are doing. This is better than the golden rule in that it has an itch, unreachable by you, not go long without a great scratching.

happens. If she tries not to have an affair because he doesn't want her to a very heavy, nonheavenly burden is placed on the relationship. If you are going to get your relationship moving you have to travel light. If she doesn't have an affair because she thinks she shouldn't she will continue to have mental affairs without physical tests.[5] Attempting to block an imagined affair both in the mind is an attention thief having his way with you at a deeper level, with a pregnancy of suffering and soon the birth of pain. Resolving your internal with your external inspires and takes all the attention you can find, create or steal. It isn't hard to live on Earth when you have discovered the mischief the mind gets up to when you're away. When you are checked out all kinds of things can happen, but worse yet when you are checked out you come back without the relevance and context you had right before you left. You have to get those back which typically takes exactly the amount of time that you are present.

I had a good idea in college; one per semester gives you an "A," two gives you a "B," three and you are average. I tried training a hamster to do several tricks, then I put it in the cold so that it would hibernate. The idea was to find out what effect hibernation has on learning. Hibernation turned out to be trickier and longer than I expected. As it was, the hamster seemed to remember nothing of what he had learned before, including breathing. I had a little ceremony for the now deaf and dumb little guy and buried him along with the idea, almost. I tried the same thing with a caterpillar pre-cocoon. Problem was I couldn't really find it within myself to try and teach a caterpillar anything. I hadn't had kids yet, nor could I figure out what I could teach it that a butterfly could do too. I figure that given how much time people spend checked out, this type of

---

[5] Stress is always the result of a possibility in the mind not sufficiently tested in the body. It is a negotiation without verbs with no body listening.

research could be very fruitful, especially when traveling through the vast expanses of outer or inner space.

The entire cultural structure is based on the apparent fact that you have a choice, meaning that your behaviors are influenced by your thoughts. Without this presupposition there would be no law,[6] no advertising and no almost anything. With this presupposition there is nearly universal suffering, unhappiness, war, trauma, hate, empty lives and an overall shallow existence. The price for this felonious presupposition is high so there must be an equally high payoff. There is: You get to remain on Earth and always have something to bitch about. Almost everybody talks more about their problems than anything else and all problems are based on some version of this primary mistake. A flaw in the very foundation of your philosophy influences everything else rather drastically. It just doesn't matter how pretty the house is if it falls on your head.

What could you do if you could separate your thinking from your behaviors? You could do much what you do now, other than suffer, and you would free your thinking, really let it go. The farther out your thinking goes the more entertained you will be. Soon you would have a life well worth living and you could get on with spirituality. There is no more ineffectual person than one who has been convinced that he or she can do something about something that he or she cannot.

A prisoner comes to depend on the ball and chain.

Thieves should sneak around quietly, you know that. So too should enlightened people be perfectly silent, but you should be yelling at the top of your tongue all the time, screaming given what you see in relation to what there is. This sort of injustice is worse than any holocaust or racial slur. If you yell selectively, people will listen even more selectively; it is more of the same. If you scream all the time then you are like a pressure cooker

---

[6] There is already no order.

CHAPTER 20

under too much pressure and though nobody is listening, it still relieves you of some of the burden you are carrying on so. If the sound of the pressure cooker releasing bothers you, the best solution isn't to block the release holes because if you do there will be one large release hole. If you learn to listen to others speaking, and yourself, as the daily pressure release valve you will love the sound and listen when you want and not when you don't want. You will be much less likely to be blown up without due process.

You are a courier, a contagion, there is a chance that you know what you are carrying but it is a small one. There, too, is a chance that you can put it down but it is a smaller one. There is too a chance that you will run a light-year mile but nobody is betting on the sure thing so the odds do a capitalist flip and all of a sudden you like the longshot without the payoff. You can enter an underdog in a dog show, but he will only be the odds on favorite in the field of expectation trials, and you just don't have a ghost of a chance to do anything but put yourself up for stud. Put a bounty on your head, call it a celebrity auction and find out if you can't get some sort of work done before you are called.

Many years ago I was blown away in Boulder. There was a 115 mile per hour wind. It was a long night, conditions outside were so bad that all I could do is close my eyes and look for a place to stay. I ended up in the county jail, locked up but with a place to rest my head. Motels weren't taking any windfall and my only chance at that point was any chance I could get. I met new friends, I explored my criminal side, rolled over, wasn't rolled and considered myself luckier than anyone else in the cell.

Compared to the spiritual abundance available here you are paying full price for the little "guess what" box and wondering why you are both afraid to look and afraid not too. The common denominators in looking are the fear and you. There are so many things that you do instead of meditating or praying

171

because they seem to make so much sense. God seems to have become nearly deaf and you can't hear others praying either. There is but one way out: In. You need to turn into yourself once you have taken care of your surroundings. This is a paint-by-number in code. The South will not rise again, either geographically or in test scores. It can't because it is composed of too many people not willing to give up, or keep up, the fight for all the wrong reasons.[7] Fight hard, fight long and then, in a moment of exhaustion, exhumation and expassé run for your life until you fall over and then you will be at the "You are Here" place ready to start your journey.

You define yourself by what changes. You define yourself by what goes on around you. You define yourself by what you think. You define yourself by anything which happens to get your attention; and you defend. What if it didn't have to be this way? What if the moat doubled as a lap pool for both sides? What if the eye of the storm was all that you could see and you could see your way clear through everything that currently blocks your vision? What if you had a third eye that cut through everything? What if you stopped defining yourself by movement and could sit right where you are forever almost laughing? What if you couldn't reach for anything because it had all already arrived?

I am telling you that life is sweet, so sweet already and so missed that the only possible tragedy is repetition. You go here, you go there and you miss both. It is time to open your eye, time to get on with nothing at any cost. You never really use what you have, saving it for a rainy day, and, it is raining like hell all over the world. Did you know that at any point in time on Earth there are between three and four thousand thunder-

---

[7] When you give anything, especially an emotion, a name, you have given it an unearned title, an alias, making the real you harder to find and the superficial you everything but more obvious.

storms? That is worth knowing, not just when you are in one but all the time, and especially if it is raining pets where you are and you call somebody long distance who happens to be basking in your lost sun.

If you can behave in context already you have to learn how to get out of it and interrupt anything that seems to be going on. If you are hiding you need to seek and if you are already seeking you need to hide. Now, your discontent is nearly perfect, you are unhappy if you win because you might not next time and have to pay taxes and you are unhappy if you lose because you just don't like losing. The only time you think you will be satisfied is if you are not playing but you have to play. Your optimism is enough to get you going but, and this is lucky, not enough to carry you through. This is good news because it means that you have to pay attention to something other than what you already are to find yourself where you really are in the face of profound knowing. You will be forced to let go, you will be forced to relieve others of the need to whisper or pass anything relevant to you. You allegedly live,, but right next to you, in the same spot you are in, is this ghost, ever closer to where you really are than you or anyone can know. You are haunted by the perfection of all things. It is so close that you can smell it, taste it, see it, hear it and feel it but you can't think it, not just enough yet. This perfection torments you and results in either a perpetual "this isn't it" or a general, thus unnoticeable level of dissatisfaction entirely independent of everything. You can't win because no matter what you win you still can't know what you need to know which is: That everything is perfect just the way it is. You hate change as you feed on, off, it.

The boy teases the dog because he loves it. The dog gets mean and bites the boy. The boy gets mean and hits the dog. The dog bites the boy harder. The boy screams, the dog is put to death after quarantine and the boy gets a new dog.[8] There is something odd about the way mankind treats his best friend. The male man, dog's best friend, is shunned as a mere carrier of possibility. It is no accident that so many shootings happen in the post office. How could it be otherwise since it isn't certain whether there is good news or bad news coming until it is too late? The male man feigns objectivity and precision but really doesn't care what is in your mail. A bill, a love letter or a sweepstakes con, it is all the same to him. You act as though you are always delivering a message from on high somewhere in there really knowing that you have never been on high and that if you had everything would be different. If you are on the mountain enjoy the view; if you are deep in the swamp enjoy the view. Anything worth opening is worth not reacting to. You keep waiting for the letter from Jesus calling you home, it's Sunday and there is no mail that day.

Another business day arrives, another tick-tocker of the calendar. You are getting older but not a bit wiser. You can even get smarter without getting wiser and what good will it do you? There are rewards and punishments that you depend upon for your lack of sustenance. You may want to discover soon that you're really your own customer. If the band isn't happy with the music they are playing they aren't happy. If they aren't happy they won't play very well; if they don't play very well they won't be happy and what have you done to yourself today in the name of getting something done? And what have you done for yourself in the name of nothing at all? Balance these.

There is nothing to do, there is nobody to "be." The race is over and the results will always be announced. You did your best, it was both good enough and not. In other words:

---

[8] The same works with spouses. Please don't hesitate to generalize or particularize anything I say to life in your life.

Indeterminate. The jury is in, they have nothing to say. Ye have been judged and not been found anything but you.

Market research shows that five out of every people really don't like four out of every five people but they pretend to because they think that they should. I invite you to suspend the gravity, not gravy, of your thinking for a bit but be careful because things that you were holding up won't define you, holding you up, anymore. They won't fall either. You must suspend, after obeying,[9] all "natural" laws or you will not be able to notice the spiritual laws. None of the rules from this tunnel apply in the next. Nothing that is important in this tunnel is important in the next. Nothing that is in this tunnel is in the next. You are entering a tunnel, a new tunnel, turn your lights on so you don't have to wait for the light at the end. Slow down, letting the tunnel call the shots. You are either ready for spirituality or you are not. If you are you are in for a treat. If you are not you are in for many treats of a different kind. In spirituality there is just one treat because there is just one. If you still need many, which is what is available on Earth, then you will spend more time there.

It is time for you to be incarnated within this life, then reincarnated. The time is now, the leverage is freed from its worldly workings and ready to lift you up, you who think so little of yourself and so often. You who are number five on America's most wanting list, you who has perpetually delayed satisfaction but not suffering. God loves you but she doesn't like you very well, she can only like you as much as you like yourself. Man is God's best friend and the bone she will give you is spirituality. This bone will point at the marrow of life instead of waiting for the morrow. When your hope is gone, when your dissatisfaction no longer defines you, when you have seen red and charged then read to this point, you are ready to take the leap

---

[9] Obeying, then abeyance, that is the order of growth.

of faith to whatever comes next. You are ready to grab for the ring as you go round and round and round. Are you dizzy yet? Are you ready for a little spiritual respite that you don't have to under-stand and control? Yes, I think yes is the answer. Say yes to everything, say yes when you want to say no, say yes when you don't want to say anything at all and say yes when you want to say yes. That way and that way alone you will at least pretend that the seduction is complete. Even at this level pretending counts as long as you remember that it is pretending. Say YES, loudly, lonely and regardless of context. Say yes no matter no, or what. Say yes to Earth and you are ready for spirituality. Even one no on Earth and you discover that order does matter. With one no there is no kidding anymore, senses disappear: sight, sound, smell, taste, touch and humor. You are being chaste with no place to hide but all alone. Spirituality is putting you off for this very reason. It is declining to set a date or even date you. She isn't pissed but thinks she deserves better than even the possibility of no and she is right as always, yes, she is. It is time to say yes, fill your head with yeses. Fill your database with yeses. When you have, like Johnny Appleseed (JAS), spread yes far and wide you will be ready for spirituality. Say yes to what you like and what you don't like and you will discover that what you defined yourself by just took away your finesse, having you bluff listlessly. Have you had enough, too much and just RIGHT? Until you can see your wife as the "other" woman you don't get the other woman or your wife. The other woman is spirituality, she is your salvation here on Earth once you don't want to leave. You will have to leave your chips on the table, letting them fall where they may as you fall effortlessly forward into a world in which there is no knowing only yessing. *Hint:* Say, "Yes, sir." as loudly as you can: this is all basic training for another life, this other life you get when this one is finally noticed as perfect. Are you ready for spirituality?

CHAPTER 21

The Good News

If there were a gun to my head, and it would still count if the finger were my own, and I were given the ultimatum, and it would count if the voice was mine or not, that if I finish this chapter I must die I would finish this chapter: read on.

While this may sound a little melodramatic most of what passes for life on Earth is a melodrama competition and if you are winning you are losing and if you are losing you are just bad melodrama and either way Darwin isn't listening and neither is anyone you would want to reproduce with so what is the point?

I am only writing this to get the chicks. Have you heard of the wet and wonderful benefits of the women who hang out around little known writers seeking to be ever so much more beautiful and satisfy that author's every want and need both sexually and when it comes to anything else on Earth? I am just making this up but I am believing it and that spurs me on in a beautiful and somewhat tragic way, but without melodrama.

Aren't you glad that we aren't each a little more like Christ? Because if we were then there would be a line for resurrection and somebody probably would have found a way for it to be more taxing than it must be already, and I wouldn't like that but I am not counting on that because really, when you come right down to it, I am living rather well this time around making anything that happens after this gravyland.

Really though, I would die for you but I wouldn't die for your sins because, other than your thinking that you have them, I don't see that you have any at all. Maybe though, I am just not that good at seeing sins, and maybe to really see sins you have to deny yourself something in the name of something else so that you can get well and truly pissed at anyone who hasn't. Well, I am not the kind of bear who does that and I am not the kind of bear who sleeps around on the first date either. But I am very careful about who I hibernate with and I am certainly even more careful about who I would let read this, if not what I would write and all of this is for both your and my sake equally. As I write this I love you so much that there is no alternative but to write on and anytime there is no alternative at all my life is so much better than when there is, but that is only because I am more than willing and able to take any alternative in the face of any other one without preference or concern for the future which I put my life and pledge my troth too.

If you don't live at the edge of something then you won't be taxed as such, and if all you are is driving distance from the edge then each moment is deprived of the significance it might have which, as you sum it and live it, robs you of everything I would call a life and precludes you from getting wise but hastens you regretting old. Life is both too long and too short to live with regrets. Because if you do, there is a role of threats here and anything that you did under the influence of a threat doesn't count and most things that you do are under this influence, you will regret everything or bore people with that which you think you don't regret, making them regret and that is no way to live a life.

Hint: Should you wait, even for a moment, to live, should you wait, even for a moment to have more sex, should you wait even for a moment to do exactly what you want exactly when you want to you will learn less than you could here on this Earth and you, and I, deserve better than for you to have done that.

I am not suggesting, as some will say, that you grab for the gusto, I am suggesting that it is from the ledge when you finally get up to the choice to jump or not and it looks, sorry dear reader, as though it is equally likely that you will and won't that the lights in the city or in the country look as beautiful as they can and your son or daughter looks worth hugging and your mistress looks worth avoiding and your memoirs look unnecessary and hot chocolate tastes the best it ever can or could. It is strictly on the face of such a choice that the face of the clock smiles at you and you escape, forever, different degrees of forever dependent on your use of consciousness, the meta-mundane escape of thinking and move to a scape where you don't see who is listening but you know somebody is finally listening to you in such a deep way that it matters more what you say next than anything else. If you can go on in that moment. If you can speak when you know you are being listened to then you truly are at worst the son or daughter of God and you will never again take the bait risking the springing of the trap because you will have escaped a world in which there are traps and admit that there is this place where there are only rewards and admit too that you live there forever if you like it or not.

While this may seem too good it has only scratched the surface just deep enough to let in an infection or anything else that comes along seeking shelter in you.

You can get there from here.

It has all worked out already.

You are to celebrate, loosely defined, from here on because we have arrived. To deny it even one more moment is a luxury you can't afford. You can tap out with confidence, SOS, and ignore the kind of nostalgia that makes you think you will get another chance in the face of no evidence to the contrary. Though still defining ourselves as a survival tip up, our Earth sphere of influence reveals that we have so much influence both by what we do and what we don't that tenure couldn't be any better than this. Mortality itself has become a luxury in a world where our every whim is produced in sufficient quantity to bring the price down to the point where anybody could afford it. When this specific number of whims that have gotten satisfied do then we have to admit that this is one heck of a species?

LET'S PLAY A LITTLE game here: I will write the next four sentences in some order: you figure out what the order is and I will tell you in a footnote what the real order is; in the process you tell me if you want to be my editor, OK?

(1)When we could have played ringtoss she wouldn't or couldn't. (2)Now it is time to be happy. (3)It used to be, when we were still plagued by survival, that one who could destroy it owned it but now we are full circle, ringing out or joy for all the galaxy to see, "We can have, make, do, be anything we want." (4)Yes, I got an e-mail from the blonde the other day and yes it has been several years since I didn't do her, but, and aren't I rich, she wants to know how she can be happy because, believe it or not, she isn't very happy and now, maybe too late, knows it. —1— Now that I am busy in other shafts, mining the kind of jewels and delights that I have never even imagined before, she would like a little attention.

Wouldn't you like a little bit of attention? Can't you imagine that I am writing this only for you and can't you further forget, in your purely and perfectly human way forget

---

—1—The real order is—3-2-4-1 so it should read like this—(3)It used to be, when we were still plagued by survival, that one who could destroy it owned it but now we are full circle, ringing out or joy for all the galaxy to see, "We can have, make, do, be anything we want." (2)Now it is time to be happy. (4)Yes, I got an e-mail from the blonde the other day and yes it has been several years since I didn't do her, but, and aren't I rich, she wants to know how she can be happy because, believe it or not, she isn't very happy and now, maybe too late, knows it. (1)When we could have played ringtoss she wouldn't or couldn't.

that you imagined it and consider it real? Please, think of this as a letter to you, strictly to you, from whom you most wanted a letter when you most needed it. And please, and I will leave space for this write in the place of the next sentence that I might write exactly what you need to hear right now.

When is the last time I told you I loved you? When is the last time I told you I trust you? Good Lord I trust you with my book. If I don't tell you often enough you forget who is sending these words along to you and right before you forget that you forget who the words are really meant for. This is, just between me and you. And, I am, hurting in a very good way because it is. Each day you must exceed the best you can possibly imagine happening and you do and on any day that you notice that you did then it is a day in which you will have no choice but to celebrate and the very fact of this day and another is the celebration. It used to be that my daughter, when very young, just enjoyed each day and lived it to the fullest; now, as a teen, she kind of picks each day apart finding the perfections in it that she can and it is always enough ranging from a call from the perfect acned boy to a long deep and perfect cry. The good news, among others is that it used to be that your dissemination of good news used to be limited by a man named Gutenberg that now anyone can spread the word. It used to be that you were protected by only one Paul Revere and now every reporter is on. It used to be that you had to go to dinner alone, now, like I often do, you can go with Mr. Heimlich guaranteeing that no matter what you are eating and how well you are chewing you will make it through to the end.[2]

This is a bull market, which means that any bullshit around is just a sign that it is really safe to live fully invested and to not

---

[2] His insurance is not eating. He doesn't eat because he doesn't want to do on to himself as others are doing on to others in his name. And he certainly doesn't want to put you in the ponderous position of finding out if you would save his life if you could.

hold back even the least little bit. If you hold back, plaque can't be far away and you will have to defend your heart from a siege, an attack, of the worst kind. If you use your heart, if you invite anyone into it who gets near it then it won't really matter how long you have lived, you will live well. You have all been in the presence of a child who lived fully. If that is beautiful then being in the presence of an adult or even more so an old person who has lived such is the only kind of honor that you need or deserve for yourself. You haven't squandered anything, any-thing you ever had you still have. Any chance you ever missed will only be missed again if you dwell on missing it. It is never too late to open 24-7, are the first two numbers of your locker combination and it is never too late to find out that any third number will do.

The moment one person made it into a spiritual game we had arrived. While this was a long time ago the repercussions have traveled sufficiently to be available everywhere and they are so free that the lowliest worm on the planet can drink deeply of them. Finding out you have won the lottery would be demeaning in the face of what is yours now, but de meaning doesn't last long in the face of your light and lightness. Yes, the blonde wants me, yes the blonde wants you too, and yes she can have both of us and all of us because you cannot possibly escape Earth until everything that can happen does, and it has and it does. So, so what, so everything, sew a beautiful quilt that will always keep you warm and always be there.

You can no longer hide from yourself except for enjoyment in the face of the knowledge that you have been found and can't really be lost again. You have sinned often enough, and any sinning is just target practice. You can't lose here for the real game has already been played, the results have already been posted and you could see them if you wanted to. In other words: The future is all yours and in it you still prosper.

Beethoven wrote for you. Picasso and Rembrandt painted for you and life disrobed for you. Isn't life grand each moment whether you know it or not? You won't pop, though you often feel that you will as you inflate with a combination of good and bad news together in just the proportions you need to learn about your whole existence and to justify anything you want. You can make up new words, new pictures, new feelings yourself anytime. There is no human law which restricts this and no physical or biological or botanical law that does either. You can change your skin, you can shed your life and you can step up to the plate each moment for the game winning risk of hitting the Hell out of it or striking out, immortal either way. You have all had the everloving shit beaten out of you but it is still there, waiting patiently to be obviously everloving again. Anything good waits forever to be expressed, anything bad is just something good not yet discovered.

The Eleventh Commandment, which amends the first ten is Thou Shalt, which is a never-archaic way of saying, "Yes." And when you have said yes you have said ALL.

We have arrived. It sounds more like a threat than it should. But now the real work begins, the work of acknowledging that we are one. If you are safe then you should be; if you aren't you shouldn't be. Just the perfect thing shows up each moment.

I cut my son's hair. His 9 year-old eye didn't like it. It isn't about the hair I know. I remember when my father cut my brother's hair too short and a baseball cap was worn for two weeks. My father never cut any of our hair again, giving us all a shearing for my brother's alleged vanity.[3] If God gave you a bad haircut would you complain? You aren't allowed to say that God doesn't give bad haircuts because anybody, on any given day, and even God might not keep up with the case of your

---

[3] Is it an accident that now, at past fifty my brother, not his keeper, wears his hair long and often has a baseball cap on?

particular bad day sufficiently to stay ahead of your adjective
doling enough to stay away from the bat of your badness. It is a
bad haircut if you call it one, at least in your world which is
what I am trying to get into here. And not just your world. I was
walking along perfectly, having edited three chapters, had
perfect sex, swum a mile, thinking about how thin I am and
how rich I will be as you read this and how rich I am in all other
ways already, when I found a way around all this. How about
cutting his hair so that it will take time to grow back to a length
he likes and empowering him to give me grief at least part of the
way until then? Yes, that would do.

You get upset, then you look around for something to blame
it on. It wasn't my brother's haircut that bothered him, it was
just an adolescent, not hormone free, zone, this complaining he
found himself in. The same is true for my son but in the
present case it was both expressed and acknowledged which
leaves my son to have his hair anyway he wants and to further
admit in very non-therapist tones that he really doesn't care
about his hair but he does care about me and he was hurt by the
fact that a visiting friend wasn't really mature enough to play
with though he has exactly a decade of supposed knowledge on
my son. He was sad because things don't always turn out the
way he expected and that he will continue to expect and they
will work out the way they do.

He cried a lot, about his hair, I cried because he doesn't yet
love you the way I do, all of you, and I marveled at the way that
when we need a good cry just the right stimulus wanders along
at just the right time.[4]

My son loves me. We went skunk hunting on the eve of the
haircut. After dark and wandering through the fields of home

[4] This, though always true with adults, is much more obvious with kids. My
daughter knows precisely when she needs to be upset and makes certain it
happens. So do you. You may as well admit it because I know it already and
you will soon if you don't already.

with two flashlights and two small caliber rifles. We saw a bunny and shot two little temporary holes in the pond but we had flashlights, the day before Halloween and the moon was one day away from full and we were already with love for each other and if that isn't life, and if it didn't take us a long time to not get a skunk and if your trip even had any degree of bad smell then I don't really know what life is about.

The length of time that you can't laugh at something is the indication that you need glasses to bring it either farther away or closer or both alternately until you can see it first for what it is, then for what it isn't and then, and this is the good news, for anything at all. There is still plenty of room on the canvas to paint anything.

My son loves me and as long as anyone remembers that or ever knew that it still is: always. He gets upset sometimes and forgets. He forgets who he is, then who I am then who we are, but just as quickly he remembers and the fertile crescent of life on the edge returns. Sometimes, especially if you listen to the other news, the news of Earth you forget too. You forget the good news. You need to be reminded. You would like his hair depending on your mood. You would always like him, though you might not know it. He is as undeniable as water, as persistent as celestial time and as playful as an otter in the first snow. He has freckles on either side of his nose and God's eyes. Eyes that if you look in them once going blind wouldn't have you miss anything worth seeing.

The selfless-inspired fog is clearing, tomorrow will be fine, it is being taken care of, coddled as we speak today. It is insured for more than anything ever has been. If you can still get upset about your hair or a pimple or anything then you have forgotten the most important thing. There is only good news, time will bare me out on this. Time will bare you out of anything and into something else which lets you forget anything. It's slightly easier to forget the good than the bad. You just swap out one piece for the other, one bit for the next bit. Your bits are edited before you get them. They are tailored to fit your philosophy but there are always and only seven of them. As you grow into your new role, as perfect, you will edit less and have more energy. It takes energy to edit and it consumes energy to even see through the edits. You will edit less each moment just having read this far and life will be an uphill easy. You have no idea how much your mind has had its way with you and how the result of such an intercourse is always trouble and discourse. You can let go now. You can let your sounds rush forward into pictures and your pictures flood your body and your body rush inspiring others to build arks, and just throw your head back and enjoy the reign of perfection all around you.

You are the Father, the Son and the Holy Ghost but a bad haircut is enough to have you forget this, so, oddly is a good haircut. Can I tell you a secret?

Nobody really cares about your hair not even you.

On our skunk hunt we saw a hare, though I think, given his day, that all he saw was a rabbit. Out of respect for the little harmless beast and all of the rude animal loving people in the world we didn't have time to get a shot off. "Hugh, the bunny ran away."

Your view of good news and bad news is determined by factors beyond your control long before you ever even find out what the story is. You are predisposed to such a degree that you are nearly never naked in the eyes of your own spin.

The good news is that you are more changeable than a chameleon. The good news is that you are deep enough to dive in and shallow, fast, enough to touch bottom. You alter faster than your surroundings but pretend that you don't. You move through life without moving and then you move two, relationship, doubling your fun. Remember, you won't remember much of this when you wake up. Now, you remember much of yesterday but next week you won't and you already remember tomorrow in a very odd way. It is just the ability to borrow things from the universe that makes Earth such a darn good place to be.

The worst news that I have for you is that there is a safety net of sorts (remember sorts) which is composed of the connections between each thing and every other thing making it impossible for you to fall and hurt yourself: ever. You are woven into this safety net making you roughly equivalent to if not inclusive of all other netters.

I had a butterfly net when I was a kid. Just thought you might want to know that.

You have to grease the whole thing, net the connection, but first you have to have enough spiritual currency to afford the grease. The economy on Earth is based on yes and no. A balance between the two keeps contraction and inflation in check. Inflation is growth without basis, contraction is basis without growth. Spiritually speaking, which isn't easy, you have only yes. Yes is the monetary unit in the economy of the spirit. Spirit is the manifestation of reality in any location. For this manifestation to, sorry, manifest, your thinking can't leave a Marx but must rise quickly enough past ideology, repetition and anything else, showing that you can let go of thinking entirely. You must fall forward and backward into breath, void, consciousness, love and up all at the same time. All life on Earth is dependent on opposition.[5] In spiritual play there is no opposition. The amoeba keeps its specific tension by putting a wall between inside and outside and controlling how this balance gets played out. Your

---

[5] The other very early morning in the hot tub I got a glimpse of the stars as one-celled animals. This mating of large and small seemed more liberating than leaving my fate or the demeanor of the day up to what any lesser scale might have to say. I am now looking for a scale that weighs in tons making my weight decimals or fractions all less than one, I hope.

own mem brains will be semi-permeable and the more permeable the better the life. There is always good reason to shut down but that isn't what reason is for. You have where you live and where you don't live, on a psychophysical level you balance these two out with your fences. Between man and woman there is an element of control, between you and anything you perceive to be food or food for thought yet another.

These boundaries set up, institutionalize imbalance that makes Earth what it isn't to such a degree that nearly nobody sees through it. If they do, they better be quiet or ostracized. Spirituality is a non-place of no such opposition, no imbalance, no institutions and no anything. It would be funny what people on Earth have done with churches and religion if it wasn't such an abstract representation of what it seeks to portray once things are at best believable. Harder to believe and hardly to believe are both happier than believing.[6]

So, you use the yes to buy the grease which you smear all over the safety net, thus allowing yourself to slide through into a world where winning has no opposite and it takes no time to get there. Any representation you make of this in your head isn't it because all representations are based on the transference between cells which always has to do with balance, imbalance and the time it takes for such weather to work itself up, wind itself down. Spirituality is the creation of a brain with one cell so that the thinking that takes place there is not defined by various imbalances, pressures or synapses but strictly by the unity unnecessary and inherent in one. While this is fundamentally possible and actually what happens the appreciation it receives is psychological in nature and disease-implied. In other

---

[6] Belief is a huge chunk, it contains so much unexplored terrain that you don't really ever know what the big payoff and cost are, you just cease to observe in its presence making you less healthy, less wealthy and more dumb. When you break your beliefs down, way down past their knees you will find out what it is to really be holy.

words: Enlightenment is much closer to craziness than is your everyday life. It seems off that we have come to such a place that we have to medicate people for our own sake when they show signs of growth.[1]

I have told you before that soul is the smallest unit that you can currently perceive. When soul gets to the cellular level the brain becomes a bunch of little brains, little in size not ability, making you into billions of different people all communicating with each other at the speed of light and reaching a non-representative consensus that begs all questions for such a diversion and lack of cohesion that we should be thankful to our politicians for doing the grotesque job they are doing because someone has to be at the bottom of the evolutionary scale and if they volunteer for such duty who is to deny them.

BRIEF INTRODUCTION

Your illusion is taking a hit here. You are still waiting to be picked for a team and you are the unknowing captain. Your illusion is getting hit so often, so hard, from so many directions that you decide that it must be reality. Sample rate defines what you think is there. Anything that shows up on your radar often enough to be, it seems wrongly, seems worth dealing with. This is the nature of illusion and illusion is not of nature at all. Your illusion may not be as big as other people's but you aren't supposed to covet. When you stop coveting I have some really good stuff for you that you don't have yet so please read on. Your illusion isn't as big as some other people's but it is still just the

---

[1] Function should be the most natural form of expression there is and when it isn't that is only because we are so busy doing things we shouldn't be doing where we shouldn't be doing them that we can't even bring a benchmark in to do a little surveying and have to depend on our ever-altering perception of the lay of the land which all too often is whoever we laid last or didn't lay depending on where we come down on the pessimist question and where we rise up on the optimistic: one.

right size to get stuck in your throat, stuck in your head and just plain stuck. Enema is not the singular form of enemy. Enemy is both singular and plural which scares me. Enema and enemy just come from the wrong end, attention to the end, fear of the end or waiting for the end. It will always be later than you think because thinking slows the perception of, but not the process itself, down. With thinking it is always too early or too late without ever being just the right time. Have you ever had an itch that no matter how hard you scratched it it didn't seem to satisfy it? I had one of these under a callus on my big toe the other day, it would have driven me crazy if I hadn't noticed a delightful though initially tiny humor in it. This itch is life on Earth. It is your life, it is the life of anyone who has not died.

The star fell for you. It burned so that you could make a wish, it is the birthday candle on the cosmic cake and it is your invitation to spirituality. Your seductive note from the universe hummed just so that you wouldn't be able to turn your back on it or turn it into something else. Yes, this is the way it goes, tough luck it is your birthday again, come out from the shadows and find out if you cast one what will come back. Your shadow and your reflection in everything is there this cold winter day and in summer too, the good news is that there will soon be another day with a different reflection of you in it. The better news is that there is today because there could not be another day unless there were. Earthbound existence is one in which there is only tomorrow and never today, so you must have escaped or been re leased. This shows, irrefutably, that spirituality is closer to where you are now than in earthly existence and if that isn't good news it isn't news at all. With earthly existence being tomorrow's diet, purchase or such, today is spirituality, I am so glad you came.

Jesus said, "I'll be right back." That left mankind but in a quandary trying to live off of tips until the real thing comes along again. While this doesn't sound smart, it doesn't sound like fun either. I say, get out of the doorway if you aren't going to go all the way through. If you are going to move slowly let me buy: something. "In case of fire, handicapped people leave last." Darwin said that, sort of, but nobody who is currently alive listened.

An Above the Footnote to Those Still On Earth

If this is the good news then the bad news isn't really worth hearing.

Worldly maturity leads to spirituality. Worldly immaturity leads no anywhere that isn't worth being. In an attempt to dominate the experience of another you do almost anything to get attention. Once you get the attention you are embarrassed at your own existence. If you don't get the attention you fight harder. To cure this ugly, familiar cycle all you have to do is discover yourself as a giver of attention rather than strictly as a receiver. While this is easier for those who have had the perfect luxury we don't really have the luxury of that. You have to learn to give attention even though you have endless thoughts and conversations about not having gotten enough. That is one of the reasons that I suggest you get laid often. That way you will have filled up a metaphorical container which is enough to inspire you to open a deeper though less obviously metaphorical container moving ever closer to who you really are. As the metaphors fill the "real" you starts to show up. You have to fill one metaphor container for the next deeper one to show up. There is a tendency to make more containers without being sufficiently creative or intelligent to fill the ones you have but this makes a logistical mess which though providing a lifetime's worth of work won't even scratch the surface of a life worth living, or a moment really worth living.

The good news is that you can get there from here. The other good news is that there are so many ways, but that is bad news too because for every way there is there are 852 diversions. If you do the math that too is a diversion. You can get there from here but as a part of AA (Alive Anonymous), you will have to first admit that nearly everything you have done in your life has been an unhealthy appetizer to bide your time until the real meal, spirituality, was served. The good news is that it has been served just not by you. Now it is time to start serving.

A guy I met in college was afraid of contracting anything. He always audited courses, not getting any credit for them, and he always wore a prophylactic. He didn't just wear it when he was having sex, he always wore it. The good news is that you can take it off unless you are messing around with something truly dangerous and then leave it on for as little time as possible. St. Peter will thank you if you follow this little piece of good news.

In other words: You can stop trying to defend yourself with your prophylactic no. The only thing you need to fear on Earth is people who fear Earth. They are the dangerous ones. Take it off, let it go, release yourself to play. Say yes. But until you learn how to say yes first and foremost without evaluating first, learn the secret lesson of watching your no's. It will make you cross-eyed but it won't make you cross, angry, mad or upset like living life into lies has.[8] Now get going, nowhere, but make sure you know where the brake pedal is. First let's take advantage of your opening, then check out your brakes.

---

[8] Judson was well and truly red-faced mad the other day, I could hardly see his freckles. I said, "Underneath this anger is sadness." He looked off, up and to his left for a long time, maybe 25 seconds, then looked back, opened his already wide-open eyes to tears and said, "Yes, it is," as he leaned in to hug me dearly making my life worth living once and for always.

CHAPTER 22

Everyday Path

You are always practicing something. At the beginning of anything, when you do something for the first time it is always life or death. This stage or appendage is seldom noticed and always behaved upon as a friction between who you think you are and who you might be should you fail or succeed. This friction has you waste energy without noticing, creating you as a poor actor, always performing well below your ability and heating up needlessly.

Acknowledging this early stage frees you from ignoring it and frees you to enjoy the risk without the fear. In reality there is only novelty; in illusion novelty has been given a bad rap. It is the case that each moment contains a perfectly balanced pair of life and death. This internal play is the generation of energy— life is the two sufficiently close together that vital signs show up. A heartbeat precedes a thought and the only question worth asking is whether your thinking or heartbeat will end first. If it is your heartbeat you will die a terrible death. The last second will be endless agony. If it is your thinking that dies first you will be able to celebrate anything including death from that moment on. You really haven't lived until you die well.

The acute ignorance which appears with this imbalance kicks thinking into low gear, giving you traction but foregoing speed. The senses go on hold, mitosis of the worst sort ensues,

the imaginary kind. Virgin birth, no foreplay, no sex but still
the responsibility forever seems an unfair and now volitional
trade. You speed across your particular countryside to the roar
of your unused engine in low gear, trans mission in your way.

The cure is that you have to wake up. Rules keep you
asleep, preferences keep you asleep, thinking that doesn't
threaten you keeps you asleep. It is a conspiracy by mattress
companies, car companies, perfume makers, TV stations and
nearly everybody else. I looked at Forbes magazine recently
only to discover that the first several, the big pictures, of the
richest people in the country were all corpses. They are dead.[1]
Their eyes give nothing back, their skin tone is that of an
undertaker's nightmare. To wake up you have to die. You have
to pull the plug on everything that doesn't matter but seems to.

This is a conspiracy in which the conspirators are the first
to die and in doing so further the conspiracy. A martyr often
doesn't know that he or she is a martyr until afterward and by
then it is too late. Read ahead in the script, I dare you.

Each fraction of a second you can alter this whole pull.
Earth can revolt and spin on its own axis another way. You have
two kinds of patterns that are in the way of spiritual
seduction. You have the big ones that you don't see and the
little ones that you don't see. The ones that you do see only
count in your favor, they count toward your seduction. The
angels fill the bleachers the way you do at the gridiron Sunday.
How dare football take on churches' day? Have you ever
realized how truly spiritual one has to not be to have holy time
in church and then holier time at the football park? The angels
cheer for you, they scream, "Hey, get'em." "Throw them

---

[1] If the picture was not just big but showed all of them you would see the toe
tag. As is you just have to see all the no's they have used to get to where they
are. Business, though a great sign of advancement on one level can't get you
far enough to really live. Sorry, at some level no sale.

something they can't resist." "Give me an 'R', give me an 'E', give me a 'V', give me an 'HALATION'." "What's that spell? Revelation. What's that spell? Revelation. What's that spell? Revelation." If you are even the littlest bit hard of hearing you will miss the point here. The point isn't that angels can't spell, though they are notoriously BAD spellers. The point is that if you miss their cheer just a little bit you might hear revolution instead of revelation; if you are a little too slow you might hear evolution instead of revelation. Given the power of angels and their dubious status existentially one little misinterpretation of one little glint off a gossamer wing can dominate a lifetime. The idea is that the angels will have their sport and your seduction is in their heavenly hands determining their heavenly future time.

They are cheering for you each moment, you don't even know the game is going on and you certainly don't know the rules or what position you play. Isn't it time that you admitted you are under pressure to submit to the seduction? Isn't it time that each moment becomes an opportunity to drop what you are currently making more important than anything, more current than whatever you are making important now? Isn't the very act, the act of making something important indicative of a lack of importance on its own? There are things that you make up and things that you find. If you could only know the difference between the two you would understand that seduction is a matter of speed, of going just at the perfect pace, which varies, so that you never get ahead of yourself and jump ahead.[2] With a woman (I can't speak of seducing a man sexually because I have no experience with that other than that I used to own a

---

[2] The only way you don't have to know the difference between the two is when you say yes to both. That unites them. Any other combination of yes, no and maybe separates without lifting. Remember we are speaking here of two case and points; if we were speaking of more the degree of complication would unsettle you. If you unsettle "u" you change "nut" to "not."

Nellie Fox Louisville Slugger bat, 31-inch), you have to move just at the speed that you don't think things will get better[3] later but that this really is it. Any no sets you back and spins out an "I was forced" field too broad to jump(suit) or skirt. You have to hook your finger in her leverages and leave it there until she doesn't notice it anymore. If it is your forefinger this is foreplay.[4] You need to, when she calms from the initial hook, wrap your thumb around the top of the band of the pants barely. Touching skin with the back of the thumbnail. The front of the thumb is too much, there are too many nerves there and you will not be able to resist going too far too fast. Each moment counts in a seduction.[5]

What I am trying to point out is that at the exact same time you are being seduced by spirituality you could be seducing spirituality too. After a huge storm (I was littler and that helped the size of the storm a good deal) snow was everywhere but it was the most under the edge of the roof where wind and gravity had conspired to dump a huge tailored mound. My grandfather began digging on one side of the mountain with my grandmother, not with her but they were both digging and he was digging her too. I was young so she was younger than she was to be when I was older. (Isn't life perfect in its attention to aging?) We began digging in as exact an opposition as we could. At a

---

[3] with Coke.

[4] If it is your middle finger it is middleplay, your ring finger ringplay and your little finger littleplay. If it is two fingers it is doubleplay and if it is three fingers it is bowling.

[5] If you are lying next to someone maybe romantically and you place your leg over his leg leading with the thigh, you will quickly, if he puts up with this, discover whether you own or are owned. The person with the leg on top gets a leg up and ownership at the same time. The similarity between this and a male dog marking terrain is not accidental and until now wasn't obvious either. (Please see my book *Practical Seduction* for more tips on the steps of earthly seduction and what they indicate.)

magical point, a Michelangelo moment, our hands touched in the mid-point of the mining venture. I have seldom had a better business partner than those two. We were in opposition working together and united. The result was quite a play area. Many years later I was in Marquette, Michigan, where they get real snow, the second floor window, door kind. Two kids dug into a snow bank and got assistance even though they didn't ask for it. Along came one of the huge snow blowers on the front of a county truck and ground them to bits spreading red snow nearly everywhere, even in the newspaper.

Your lessons can be fun, as with my grandparents or very difficult as with the bloody mess. The real question is what will it take to teach you something and will you know when you are sufficiently taught that the next lesson can begin? The more easily you can learn a lesson the easier the lessons will be. Imagine that everything that is really "bad" that happened in your life is somehow the result of pig-headedness on the part of someone, guardian angel? While this doesn't seem fair and it certainly isn't Kosher[6] there is an overall, generic, successful, perfect solution: The Everyday Path.

If you are very hungry you will be delighted to eat most anything. If you are not hungry and very rich you too will be very likely to eat most anything. Have you heard about what those people eat in the name of luxury? When you are hungry your standards seem to fall. One of the tricks on the Everyday

---

[6] THERE IS A SLIGHT NAME CHANGE HERE TO PROTECT ME. Gew—what if you saddled a people with a purely mind-based "religion" making thinking the prize for evolutionary boobies and then, since they come in pairs, put two of them together telling each they were the center of the universe. In a thinking world there is only one center, choice, disappears since you would rather be in the center, so the moment becomes disputed and the battle rages for who will pork who. No peace can be found in the Middle East until the Gews find some way other than confrontation to be kept the wonderful on their toes that they are. Some of my best friends are Gews but they are also, and this is universally true, their own worst enemies.

Path is to have standards sufficiently high that you won't tolerate less even though your history and probable future demand that you do. You need to be sufficiently present that you know the difference between yourself and a mole in the ground.

We once caught a mole. Well, we really didn't catch it, it sort of volunteered to be caught. It was rolling around the one place moles almost never are, on the grass, obvious by its lack of tunnel to hide in. We, as parents to a young son and daughter and now mole, looked around for toad and not finding him filled a just previously empty aquarium with dirt, grass and I don't remember what. Have you ever seen these little fellows dig? You get the idea that hyperactivity was inspired by mole himself. They move so fast, slice through the dirt on their way to nowhere so fast that it is a wonder they survive. He didn't. He was dead within hours, but he showed us that doing and living a long productive life don't really go together. You need to slow down enough to see a mole someday. Watching a mole is a better cure for hyperactivity than Ritalin, so is getting up and running around. One little suggestion from the Everyday Path is that any activity is hyperactivity because we really aren't here to get anything done. Everybody has an overproductive a(u)nt, in their past but she really isn't related to you, she can carry, marry, many times her own weight over far too long for you to compete with her by trying to get something done.

The universe is always trying to seduce you, everything on Earth is created only to that end. If you knew this, Earth would appear to be a very different place to you than it does. At the end of most adventure movies there is a romance resolution that is not nearly as exciting as the adventure. This doesn't really portray how life can be but it does show how it usually is. You are always romancing something, now you get to enjoy each moment of the seduction.

The Everyday Path is just that. You have something specific and seemingly ineffectual, and unrelated to practice. As you practice you get deeper at the specific rate that has you not notice that you are getting deeper. You need to notice and observe much more than ever but you only get to notice your growth when it has stopped, on the Platypus Plateaus, and there will be plenty of them, you get to enjoy the view. If you see your growth while it is happening you will get in the way. This same lack of logic applies to when you are shrinking. You need to catch yourself shrinking because then you can get in the way of it. Anything that you observe you retard. I once led a relationship course. The people were too obvious in their self-loathing for me to imagine, still convincing me for a moment that they really wanted relating to be even the semblance of something other than a threat. In that weak moment I looked out the window at the moon. *Goodnight Moon.* "Does anyone know what phase the moon is?" I asked. Nobody had the slightest idea, they were so busy assessing their relationships that they had failed to notice what was going on around them. You have to gaze at the moon when life on Earth is too attractive. You need to gaze at the moon, which by the way, is always gazing back at you, when you have better things to do. Really, what could possibly be better? As you get used to gazing at the moon a little more often a howl rattles up. Howl at the moon and the moon is silent back to you. The moon has no light of its own but it can blush slightly under your lover's gaze, or your own. The moon is always your friend. When I was little I camped out with a friend of mine, Mark. Mark was always more popular than I was, notice the auspicious use of past tense here. To make a long story short, my sleeping bag sort of rolled off me in the middle of the night. It was a clear clean suburban night. I got a third degree moon burn that hasn't gone away to this day. One of the results of that little camping trip is that anything that seems big and grave on Earth,

I just put on the moon, and it seems lighter and easier to bare. This is one of the reasons that people say, "He mooned me." They, as far as I can tell, mean that you really shouldn't take anything more seriously here than the moon does.

You may think I am a silly heart and you would be right. You may think that you are not a silly heart and you would be wrong.

The Everyday Path is your path, it is everybody's path. It leads nowhere but it is perfect while on it. You will stray, that is one of the points on the path. If you don't stray, if you don't forget the moment and rush ahead losing yourself and everything of value then you can't ever have a homecoming parade. Unless you lose you can't really enjoy winning. Unless you win you can't really enjoy losing. Life on Earth is supposed to be a precious, tenacious mix of winning and losing without a preferential focus on either one. One tiny decision that there is more of one than the other results in either denigrating oneself or artificially pumping oneself up. Either way you miss what is here, leave the Everyday Path and begin to set up the profound and momentary celebration of coming back to it, back to yourself, back to the ever-present offer and delivery of the seduction which is your natural right without wrong here on Earth.

CHAPTER 23

Baring the Burden of Immortality

eath is reason enough to pout. I don't care for the seeming fact that the little Magnolias we buy and plant today will be big enough to shade my grave and for my kids' kids to climb. In Georgia you can be buried anywhere outside city limits which is, incidentally, where I want to live too. More accurately it just doesn't seem fair I will miss them big. Most people don't dwell on this. They raise without looking at the cards. You wouldn't buy a rope without looking at both ends, you wouldn't tell a story that never ends, you wouldn't live a life without knowing the end would you? To spite themselves, the Magnolias, their children's children, most people, will fail to derive any delight from the little Magnolias now. They, of course, don't notice this because they are heavily invested in not noticing but knowing.

The cure for these particular, popular eccentricity loops selfishness and general lack of observation results in is simple. Probably so simple that it almost ekes by without saying: but you know me. Always have a greater love, respect and interest in all you don't notice than what you do. Also always know that what is in your consciousness is perhaps exciting but none the more mean, pitiful and mathematically insufficient set to get to happpppppppiness without slowing down the humor on the way.

You have to laugh and if you don't you will get yourself into serious trouble.

Spiritual Seduction

The most daunting spiritual reality is immortality. On Earth you use time and money as metaphors for death. You use these twins to justify not doing some things and for doing others. Anything so immediately in opposition leaves an opening which is picked up by rationality and then maintained up to the amount of discomfort you are able to tolerate. The only way to get closer to yourself is to get things further apart.

People don't start things because they don't have time and they rush through things because they don't have time. They start things because they have to get going and they stop things because they have to get going. These sorts of confusions are available all over the place on Earth but they are in ecstatic short supply in Spirituality City. My question really is, "Where is everybody going?"

Within the cultural termination writes, last rites, is the knowledge that "there is nowhere to get to" but the highest state this little ditty seems to hum is a jingle offered up by a travel agency on the musiclessness of a plane's inadequate sound system later to be hummed when you get to paradise to play craps with other people you don't want to get intimate with but will screw anytime you get a chance.

Sorry, that wasn't really a spiritual paragraph.

Regression to the mean and nasty is something worth complaining about but regression to the mediocre, though not applauded, is rewarded by an absence of attention and an absence of confrontation or the presence of patriotism or belief. One of the things we like and hate about children is that they have not yet learned, fully, to regress to the mean. Adults are much better at being worse as they regress to the mean as a way of life. Life on Earth is regressing to the mean. Spirituality is regressing to God.

While the mean is never inspiring it does seem safe. While it is never brilliant it does pay the bills, at least most of them.

While regression to the mean is common it is your odd lot too. The very existence of a mean implies too much math without a conclusion. Too much foreplay without a resolution. We have progressed from the Indian "How?" to the two-year-old's "Why?" but too often ask the question rhetorically as a mere defense against not knowing.

In other words: If you are kissing you are not talking and if you are talking you are not kissing. While talking can be a delightful interruption of kissing or even especially fun while kissing, kissing should never be an interruption of talking. The media is kissing not talking, telling. The talking is the data on the media. This is life on Earth.

In spirituality the media is praying and meditation. On Earth the media is preying and medication. If you have to interrupt your day to pray your day wasn't sufficiently current to be worth having, it was at best a mirror diversion.[1]

One of the truly odd things about living on Earth is that you know everything already. At some virginal level you already

---

[1] Between a woman's thighs lies an invitation to Heaven and one to Earth. How many lies you tell on the way there determines which it is. How many lies you tell to her is one thing, how many lies you tell to yourself is quite another. The same is true for men but more so.

Footnote within a footnote: A note to women: I only said "more so" because men need that kind of a boost. Women need it too but can't get it in nearly as easily digestible or easily assimilated form. Men can derive their inspiration from women, women have to derive their inspiration from flowers and other stuff that men haven't been sufficiently interested in to ruin yet. So, men can deflower to inspire but women must bloom. Even a late night bloomer is enough to turn a man on but a woman needs to rinse the bloomers rite out of her hair, dry them and then tend to her garden, toiling underneath the roses unable to appreciate fully what they would look like from a lateral view or from, Heaven and the Catholic Church forbid, above. Women have been oppressed for thousands of years. It may appear that by pointing this out I am creating it. This not only isn't the case here, it is never the case. I am pointing it out only because I am one of only eight men on the planet who really like women.

know everything. Between this wise you there is a silly you who has to pretend that you don't know much and that little part that you do know is everything there is. There are wise cracks, vaginal, between the boards of earthly knowledge.[2] You get bored with your boards, you get bored enough that you consider worshiping carpenters. You are either, at any point, attending to the "spiritual" you or the "earthly" you. There is no overlap between the two other than that the excrement of each is processed in the other place. Generally the spiritual world gets the rejects of Earth, the people with enough trauma, enough problems, enough suffering that they have learned there is nothing on Earth to pacify them. They seek a holy pacifying for worldly problems. The earthly world gets the scraps from the table of Heaven in the form of revelations, miracles and intuition. While these are pretty neat they are always an annoying crossbreed of inspiration and nuisance you evangelically and unconvincingly seek that others bare, carry, that you are unwilling to bare, reveal, yourself. If you want to test any relationship just try telling someone one of your revelations while it is still off the press. This is a way to always inspire another to regress to the mean. They will let you know, in an uncharacteristically fast manner, that either they already knew that or that you are crazy. Don't expect someone to fully appreciate the meal you are about to eat unless you are going to give them some, or, on Earth most of it. A substantial part of a good meal is eating it. Semi-appreciation is always semi-sweet and it leaves the scarecrow lost, in therapy, and paying alleged friends while searching for real ones.

Robert woke up, he really did, to his enlightenment. The first thing he did, silly boy, was tell others he thought were on the path. "Yes, I have had experiences like that." "No, that

---

[2] You stand in line for hours to get control, but you won't even wait for seconds to disavow any responsibility.

doesn't seem quite to be it, but keep working at it." "Goody, goody for you." They snarled these at him much to his surprise. After enlightenment you are very much like you were before, partially because you were always enlightened but didn't know it, but you are always a bit more naïve. You think that because you have arrived at Heaven that others more earthbound will be interested instead of petty, jealous and "regressing to the mean" about it. I saw Robert about two weeks after he woke up. I burst into tears and did all I could to treat him like the dignitary he had become. He said to me, "I had a lot of stuff about you but now it is obvious to me it was just my stuff. Now I really see you, and all there is there, is love." About a month later I spoke with him on the phone and he heard something other than love. He had fallen back asleep but hadn't noticed. By contrast his now dominating superficial little world snapped at me when I pointed out the obvious return of his somnambulism. It hurt me more than it did him because I noticed, got blamed, and he was only numb.

On Earth you are always leaving, so are trees, but they use their leaves to convert carbon dioxide to oxygen, growing in the process so we can process our growth. You are on your way to the mall, soccer practice, a better education, a restaurant, to get a fork, to get forked, to Las Vegas or somewhere. You are always leaving and neither here nor there. You arrive somewhere on the way to somewhere else. You get married on the way to security. You get divorced on the way to freedom. You get educated on the way to a good job and you get a good job on the way to financial security. You get financial security on the way to the good life and you get the good life on the way to death. Every "good" therapist kneads a better one into shape. You get on with death so that you can have the afterlife and life itself becomes anything afterbirth which is to be discarded because it just isn't enough on its own.

Spiritual Seduction

Spiritually speaking you are bankrupt. Spirituality begins at forty and it is the only way to have a life after that. Spirituality is selling where you are, what you have, to who you are with. earthly existence is going somewhere else to sell what you don't yet have to someone you haven't met yet who really is the one. "I got some really neat swampland in Florida."[3]

Any leaving is every leaving, by the law of metaphor. If you leave to go to the store you are leaving everything behind. Worse, you are probably not aware and not awake traveling to the store because you are waiting to get there. Finally you arrive at the store but as you are entering you look at your watch realizing that you only have eight minutes to get what you need and get out of there.

To get what you need and get out of there. That is the trick of superficial sex and life. That is a philosophy of life often lived, if you can call it that, and often expressed but not as a philosophy. It is a philosophy and it is the philosophy of most people on Earth who should be attending to spirituality but aren't.

Earth is enough to piss you off, if you pay for attention and don't get it, but not enough to feed you once you are ready for a spiritual life. Did you ever wonder why you either get angry so often or have to expend energy not to or why life seems to be fuller than it should, of shit, but not as fulfilling as it should be? On one level you are angry. If you can't stand the anger you move out one layer to where you are learning to control your anger (it is still there and having its way with you but you don't notice the huge costs to life and limb); if you just can't handle it you move one level toward more superficial and, while

---

[3] If they are the one and only that excludes you. Unless they are your one and only, which relegates you to a life of possession with an impending exorcism. The only regular exorcisms now held on Earth are spiritual enemas in which you are exorcised from who you really are so that you can become a dependent consumer kept in inventory in case there ever is shortage of buyers: tithe.

holding yourself tightly in the tensest way, you pretend that you aren't really angry at all. Tension always has to do with being in the wrong tense, not getting done what you needed to until the present has already arrived or not getting what you should have done in the present until the future arrives. Boredom is getting it done and not knowing what to do with this false self you pretended to be just to get it done until either some other worthless task shows up or some more real or artificial under-taker shows up to inspire the system to get on with things.

"How's tricks?" is the first truly spiritual question that one should ask and it should be asked about forty years of age. It should be asked so that one can discover the first rule of spirituality: Tricks, lies, deceptions, misinterpretations, tech-niques and their non-substantive derivatives don't work in the spiritual world. Using them seduces you from the spiritual world back to the earthly one. There is no pain on Earth like making this particular journey in this particular direction. You will have to do it because you enter the spiritual world while still on Earth but you don't need to invite it, beg for it, plead for it and demand it. At least I hope you don't have to because doing so is trying to sneak something less than spiritual, earthly, into Heaven. This particular crime is punishable by Earth time. If you forget that this is a punishment it makes it somewhat easier; if you don't it makes it premature Hell.[4]

If you are going down in quicksand you will grab at any-thing that might save you. If a close friend or lover of yours is going down in quicksand and throws you a rope it is easy to hold on and try and pull them out unless they are winning this tug of war and you are beginning to go down too. At that point you must either go down with them, in which case you are of no use to them, yourself or anybody else. Or, and this is not morally or rationally easy but neither is the boundary between

---

[4] Leaving anytime always defines you as a premature evacuator.

earthly existence and spirituality, you must let go of the rope and play with alternatives for saving them, you, the rope and everybody else.

Your main job, so far, on Earth, is to make certain that people, you too, don't escape. You are the jilted jailer who can't even be creative enough to serve time. Did you know that the lives of the inmates are more interesting than the lives of the guards, they have less to worry about and keep track of? You try and keep people what you call "alive" while keeping them dead. You try to have people "be quiet" if they are upsetting or may be messing with the way things are or look. You don't like things the way they are but you like them better either the way they are or the way they have been than some unknown. People's tolerance for suffering is nothing compared to their intolerance for the unknown.

Spirituality is all unknown, it is all quickest-sand. It is that way on purpose so that it strips you of your limitations and everything else on the way in. Spirituality is inevitable. If you see someone in spiritual quicker sand don't send them to a therapist, medicate them, try and fix them or ignore them: push their head downward, if you can reach it, to hasten the journey that they have to take and to, by pregression to the high mean, make it more likely that you get to go sooner and that your going gets to be made easier by their passing.

Thank goodness you don't have to die in fact, only your facts have to die for spirituality to force you screaming and kicking to rise. AMEN. Life on Earth is worth dying for and life in the Spiritual World is worth living for. "Say it like it is." It is time to leave without going anywhere, that is spirituality or oblivion. What you do in this second determines which. Your court day is set, it is today. "Yes, brothers and sisters." You are being judged at this very moment. NOW. Cross No and Ow (short for ouch) and you get NOW, the only time showing crosscontext on earthly watches and spiritual existence. *Hint:* There really isn't such a thing as earthly existence, the terms don't overlap.[5] Enjoy.

---

[5] To live on Earth you must die to spirituality; to live in spirituality you must die on Earth. Not a fictional death like your heart stopping beating or your brain function ending, but the much more real death of shifting focus from actual to possible.

Now That You're Spiritual, Let's Get Practical

oving through the air is one thing, moving through the water another. The times for a mile in water are much closer together than the times for a mile in air. The resistance of the water causes a clustering, almost clotting of times. I have noticed that the distance between me and a really good or really mediocre swimmer is nothing compared to the telescope I need for both kinds of runners unless we are running on a circular track. This bunching ensures one company if enough resistance is encountered. The counter is actually slid up by the resistance, making how hard something is give you company, or at least how hard it is to get through. To make this especially obvious race the fastest miler in the world through the door of the vault of the First National Bank of Cedar Rapids when it is closed. It is some combination of either authority or guile that will get you in there.

Defining by resistance is a purely earthly phenomenon and it just doesn't carry over to spirituality where Ease is queen.[1]

It is possible to parry with revelations forcing them upsteam until they show you more than they were supposed to about what they were supposed to and about you. A wrinkle in your whole outfit can be corrected with your overall philosophy being pleated,, hopefully correctly, the purpose of said pleat is to bring together two points which were never going to meet otherwise, thus having your philosophy fit better than it would have without the pleat.[2]

I am searching for fencing terms, on guard—ian angel, on Dancer, on Prancer and Vixen.[3] The gifts I give this holiday season are self-evident, your welcome to them is all they need. Excuse me if I seem obthreese.

I remember when the baby chickens arrived, for days I became a baby chicken of 42 years of age, which is progress from being a full-fledged chicken for many years before that. Reentry into the play market or life itself usually requires tears and tiers, salt water taffy layers of ecstasy with peace in between: imagine the best stretch of the best stretcher unmanaged making him or her ready always for anything. What if they made all clothes

---

[1] If we are going to be in love forever you may as well get my name tattooed on you. If you are going to get my name tattooed on you, you may as well get it done in large enough letters, since we are going to be forever in love, that later in life I will not have to push you away or put my glasses on to read it. Thanks.

[2] The steam is the steam used to press things, a pleat really does take two points that were not going to meet and shows how they are connected, an unintentional pleat is a wrinkle, a wrinkle out of place is a problem, and pleats really do have your philosophy fit better while giving you a much more attractive tailored look by showing more of where the contours of your life really go.

[3] It is much more likely that you will get lucky with someone who is already playing for a team than you will with someone who is giving lip service to only free agent status. You need to find someone who is already giving lip service and even tongue to someone else, in French or English, because they prefer being with someone to being without someone saying they want to be with someone. If you can find the rare single person who says that they just want to be alone then you may have a chance, but the single one who says he or she wants someone is not devious, just misguided. People can be devious and still on the right path but misguided is misguided.

only in your size? It would be easier to sort out the good from the bad news as you looked at others. There would be no more 2x or 3x, just people you have to relate to and Courtney Cox would probably look better in my jeans than either in whatever she picks to wear herself or out of them.

There is something about being crazy in public that brings out the sanity in anyone brave enough to observe, just observe. If you swerve your observation days are over and your partiality may save someone else's life but not your own, and living vicariously isn't what it is cracked up, into a tree, to be. Thank you for this opportunity taken first and then noticed, unnecessarily bayou.[4]

Culture is to your thinking as water is to your body. Culture provides the resistance if you don't have enough of your own telling you what to don't generally when your specific indicators show you the real direction to go, a short cut taken by too few to be endorsed.[5] If you can't convince your spouse of anything then you are trying to convince your spouse of the wrong thing or you have the wrong spouse and having the wrong spouse is more inconvenient to cure than learning to sell, at least some-

---

[4] "Ba, you" is what Ebenezer said in the King Dickens version of the Old Testament, but he had to say, "ba, me" first.

[5] There is no medication for a general condition—they are always philosophical. Specific symptoms with general well-being can be medicated or even mediated. The best general medication will do for a general condition is stall the symptoms, stunning observation and making it nearly impossible to notice any health in the system. You can't medicate a missing limb or link in your family tree. You don't really know what the mom is like until you have been had by the daughter. In other words: If you are told that you have tendonitis by a doctor your tendonitis is ready to leave, it has had its way with you for a long time and you have the doctor tell you about it since you couldn't notice the background of lesser symptoms on their own so he gets the credit for noticing that it exists. By the time it is inflamed it is ready to be put out. This probably goes for all specific and general medical conditions with the specific being the easiest to see and the easiest to trick or treat.

times. So get selling. Spiritual sales are no-fault sales, sales in which both parties move from whereever they are, closer to yes.

One brush with spirituality is enough to wash off all worldly stuff, ideas, scum, perspiration, difficulty and problems.

Throughout each day you find yourself in new and old situations. You have tiny wake-ups that tempt you to notice your environment. This happens hundreds and sometimes thousands of times a day. The faster you are, and the more of yourself you don't run screaming away from, the more of these you get. Every philosophy has inconsistencies, which is what has the whole field of philosophy not be as serious as it might be and life be odd enough to keep your interest. A consistent inconsistency, like thinking that one is good and pure while lying and cheating or thinking highly of oneself on top of low self-esteem is enough to turn these precious moments to threats of barely tolerable attacks on your foibles.

As you have more of these moments you will chip away at all that you have built and get going on the sculpting of your life. You have the number of these that you do, and rather than trying to figure out what that number means or what it is right now, though the number you have says everything that need be said about the evolutionary state of you, just catch the ones you do without holding any of them. A young center fielder already pegged as such needs to learn to catch fly balls one after the other, putting each down after holding it just long enough to indicate it was really a catch, so she can be ready for the next one. With practice, when she can catch a lot in a row she will be ready for the tedious, philosophical work of catching maybe four or five balls in a whole game.[6] One of the rules of the Everyday Path, if there are any, is that anything that comes along and says,

---

[6] This is one of the reasons that rules don't work. You just can't wait to apply them so you generalize with them, making them in command of your troop of thoughts and feelings rather than the present.

"Hey, look at me" is begging not to be looked at but to be used. Always raise. If something says, "think about me" or, "don't think about me," you have to do rather than just think. You have to observe deeply. Always raise again after checking. Whatever the specific environment asks for the opportunity is to demand, plead or whine for more. The general more I am speaking of here, and it isn't easy to say this so that it is understood, is that when anything presents itself there is the part of the presentation that is real and the part that is bluff. Don't call your own bluff, bluffing is what consciousness is best at, and what inspires it and what makes it what it is (and isn't). Calling your own bluff is like pestering the IRS to give you attention, it isn't really the p-p-p-p-p-p-point. Depending on how full of it you are you will have more bluff and less real or more real and less bluff. When these precious moments happen rather than freeloading on them, believing them, thinking about them, figuring them out, showing them to friends or anything else you must quickly pull the rug out from under the part of the presented that appears to be real.[7]

Never pull the rug out from under what appears to be the bluff. When you do that you reveal what you already knew wasn't real as not real which is undermining the bluff. Bluffing is one of the few genuine tools you have as an interface with reality and others' "realities." Please, please, please, don't undercut your ability to bluff. Bluffing is pretending that something is that isn't, knowing full well that it isn't but presenting anyway. This also sounds like the definition of a lie. How it varies from lying is in two important ways: First, in a bluff you are always trying to be caught. Second, a bluff is one facet of play while lying is a facet of work.

When you pull the rug out from under the part of something you thought was real, there are many things that

---

[7] Because that is the bluff.

happen. One of the first is that when you were tempted to be still you got moving: this cannot be overestimated. Always move when you are tempted to be still. Always remain still when you are tempted to move. While these two complimentary suggestions are not always true they are always true in the tunnel of illusion and there is enough illusion around that it won't hurt to apply them universally. I don't mean them universally though because it is always the exceptions that interest me most, but it is not the exceptions I write for, it is the exceptions I live for.

Another thing that giving that tug to the rug does is has you reveal connections. A rug is seldom over a beautiful hair-do. There is always something under the rug; typically, philosophically speaking, rugs are not decorative but put there to cover something up. If you look at the rug you don't see what is under it. Whatever is under the rug isn't as bad as you might think and the connections that lie under every rug are sufficient to make the rug worth yanking if you can and worth having tried if you can't.

When you give the rug a pull you will be tempted to look away from what was underneath it, the motivation for closing your eyes and shutting down in the first place. You will also be tempted to find out if anything formerly on the rug is still standing. In other words: Did you pull out the rug fast enough that what was on it, the cat maybe, is now pleasantly resting on the floor not even having noticed the absence of rug or the really fast pull? While the test of verticality of remainders is mathematically important it contains within it too great a temptation to dote, or puff up with pride at your speed and elegance.

You are a good magician, to be a great one you have to learn where the tricks take place.

So, don't look at what is left, don't look at what is revealed, don't look at how great a magician you are, don't look in the eyes of the audience. Just look, and this is the truly hard part, at the rug. This is the last place that you would look, it is the place that doesn't seem to hold anything for you. Remember when you were a kid that often unwrapping presents was much more fun than having them? Remember that as you got older you forgot that? As you have pulled the rug away, pulled it really hard, you can't keep pulling; you have to stop and if at the precise moment you stop you can get caught not in the stopping but in the opportunity to release the rug, let it go. Let go of the rug, not in a practiced manner but in a revolutionary one. Let go of it so it falls on its own recognizance, uninfluenced by you and way more often than not you will discover something magical.

When the rug falls it doesn't fall flat, it also doesn't fall loudly. It will fall some degree of folded, not a proper rug at all. When this happens and the rug is doubled over itself it presents at least double anything it was presenting. It is twice as thick where it is doubled, if part of the weave of the rug is happiness you get twice the happiness without any context-dependence. If part of the weave of the rug was anger you get at least twice the anger, again, with nothing to blame it on. The emotional upheaval from having pulled the rug out is enough to last a second: the one from the way the rug falls is enough to undermine the limitations you perceived on your own power. Attending to the folds, you will have associated two things that were formerly not even seemingly connected. In science fiction, sometimes, they talk about folding space. This is exactly what I am referring to, and the opportunity to do it shows up anytime you have a chance to interact with space.

The sooner you can get tested again, after your first test, or last test, the more accurate will be your answers because the less will be your duress. There is a specific balance point between motivation, duress and accuracy. This being the way that something traces its way into you from outside and out of you to inside. Please, let me give you a practical example. You care about someone. You don't really look at everything about that person, you look at what will be compatible with still caring. So, you put a rug down, a story, each time the person does something that isn't compatible with liking them you cover those up with something that you weave allegedly nullifying what they did. You get enough of these and you get wall to wall carpeting, meaning that you walk softly around that person whether you like it or not. Your liking the person becomes more and more bluff as your evidence for not liking them mounts. Soon, you fall behind in your attempts to mediate and your caring fades into indifference. Instead of letting this happen you can, when you have a few throw rugs around and not yet wall to wall lies, yank one of the rugs. This could be done by deciding that you don't like them, extrapolating to where you are going before you get there. But you have to decide really hard, focusing your full flashlight of consciousness, attention, on not liking them. You pull the imaginary rug "liking them" out, the rug falls, and rather than not liking them you hate them. Remember when the rug doubles or even triples on itself you magnify anything that is there or was going to be there. Hate, not being anything like the opposite of caring, you deepen your relationship. You go to great depths revealing a much deeper relationship than you were working on. Hate and love enter through the same door, you have opened the door and made whatever comes in man's best friend: be a watchdog.

Another possible rug-pull in this situation is to say out loud the stories that you have been using to excuse the people. Please don't say them out loud to make them more real, this would make you an abettor, against the odds. "I realize that I just noticed that you were lying to me and don't care about me at all because you hurt me every time you get a chance." You just pulled the rug out, you said something that you were thinking was true but that you shouldn't say. At that moment you will

Spiritual Seduction

Spiritual Seduction

always have a moment of earned intimacy making another more likely. This intimacy is from the lay of the lie, rug, once you have pulled it.

My daughter sees a physical therapist. Emily, 14, had her arm pulled at birth. This momentary stupidity on the part of the doctor influences each moment of Emily's life. We have taken her to many different specialists who performed many silly procedures on her arm. When we got to the physical therapist not only did she seem to know what Emily's problem was but she had successive cures for it. Emily fell in love with the physical therapist, which is a pretty neat thing for a teenager to do with someone who is bound if not determined to cause a lot of pain. Emily and the therapist bonded. Emily bonded at the level that she could, deeply, the physical therapist on her deepest level, Southern polite. Every other Thursday for four months they got together with Emily's arm slowly straightening and hurting plenty. One Thursday Emily showed up to find the door locked and a note on the door for another patient. The physical therapist had not only forgotten about Emily, she had remembered another patient enough to leave a note. The physical manifestation of the emotional imbalance between what Emily had to give, and gave, and what the physical therapist had to give, and gave, showed itself. Emily was hurt badly, much worse than any pain in her arm. "You are not important, not worth my time, you are only a client to me and I just don't care about you." The physical therapist couldn't say it out loud, which would have been pulling the rug out from under the imaginary relationship between the two. She couldn't.

Emily could have tested the relationship at numerous points by asking the physical therapist to go progressively or radically out of her way, discovering that she wouldn't. One of the main ways to explore is to ask the unaskable, another is to do the undoable. "This session really hurt a lot, please call me tomorrow

218

morning early to find out how my arm is." That request likely would have showed Emily that the physical therapist's caring was limited to a paid session and some words to the contrary. Or it would have made it more likely that the belle would have left a note for Emily too. If there are two people there is a deeply gravitational pull to co-conspiratorship.

I watched this happen. I watched Emily connect deeply, the therapist connect at a shallow level and knew that there would be a judgment day, an accounting for the imbalance. All imbalances will be resolved, they will be settled slowly on Earth and much more rapidly spiritually. The longer time you go without settling things out, the more excuses you can fill the till with, and the further and farther you get from how things really are. If you don't notice that you are climbing the fall is quite a rude surprise. Most people are semi-phobic of the truth, thus they resist every balance, the level terrain that would give them a place to build a foundation for a truly wonderful life.

Pull the rug out of the part that seems real and you will learn about yourself, others, the nature of things and more. Attend to the rug and the emotional doubling or tripling effect it has and you will learn easily though sometimes painfully. Emotion: Overlap between illusion and reality, is always hiding something and always ready to reveal something. The stronger the emotion, depths of the folds, the more easily things will play out as you watch rather than get involved.[8] If you get involved you will not learn anything natural about yourself. You will get flocked. Imagine getting a Christmas tree you think is pretty, then deciding that it isn't, flocking it to some horrible pink mess and then deciding that it is pretty. Can you say Mary Kay?

---

[8] A pleat is an artistic or stylistic fold. A fold is a natural connectedness of all things. If you have an idea and it looks like you should not fold it then it probably isn't worth having. Folding is a test in that it is a squaring which is the first step to geometric extrapolation.

You will cover things up in life. Pulling the rug out uncovers them. It has you not get too far ahead of yourself or too far behind yourself. The story of the hare and turtle racing isn't really about A.D.D., it is a more amoral imperative that one not let the balance get too far off without correction. When you correct by stimulus instead of response you flex the very philosophical muscles you will need to bridge the imaginary gap between mind and body. You will bridge the gap between yes and no and you will seduce the truth out of everything. The more truth something appears to contain the less apt you are to pull the rug out and the more you can learn by doing so.

Get pulling.

CHAPTER 25

Stop General Braking[1]

T he problem, if there is one, with spirituality is that when it begins to open it will not be denied or controlled. This lack of control makes it obvious that you don't have control anywhere. While this looks like about the worst news possible it is the best news. It is the best news because you have done everything that you have done without control. To get going you need to develop a confidence in your brakes. You have to know that you can slow down or you don't dare speed up. You have heard me say many times that speed is essential to any kind of spiritual growth, but you have to be able to slow up. Without this essential confidence you have to be scared or scarred, or both. You are not inclined to stay present when presented with the opportunity to free fall forward: bungee jumping with no strings attached. You are presented with this always—now it is time to give you the brakes without your applying them but knowing you can.[2]

---

[1] It is somewhere around here and sometime around now that I should, if a typical author, be concerned with split and loose ends and luckily I am not because possibly I don't have any or otherwise possibly I not only have a high tolerance for them but find them too educational for mere words.

Don't let details get in your way, clean'em up.

[2] Do and can are fundamentally different in that do robs can of trust. Without trust you might get everything done but won't learn about yourself in the process.

Spiritual Seduction

Try a little experiment with a ruler. Hold it on one end very tightly and tap something with the other end. You experience the tapping as residing where it is happening, the location of the other end of the ruler touching what it is tapping. Hold the ruler very loosely and tap something. You feel the ruler in your hand.

This simple demonstration explains why your seemingly natural tendency to hold on to things leads you astray. When you hold something your attention is drawn away from you, lost outside yourself. You mistake the object with the subject and your complete thoughts come out backwards, ruining your best laid plans and causes and effects and you don't even know enough to mourn the passing. The subject is the stimulus, the object the response, the verb the process. When you are the response you can't enter the world of spirituality, you can't get to the front of the sentence or author the thought. You are stuck on Earth. There is nothing to lessen lessons more than to make them mandatory. If, when you were little or big, you were forced to have two lollipops a day for a year, you would not look forward to the suckers nor would you want them after a while. You would even learn not to like their taste.

When I was a kid my brother and I went rock climbing. We went to a place called Devil's Lake in central Wisconsin. We clambered up little rock faces and hopped from boulder to boulder, having fun but knowing that there was more to this. Finally we found a little, maybe fifteen-foot climb that challenged us both. With a lot of fuss and strain we made it up only to discover that we couldn't go any higher on that route. We had to go back down the way we had come and it just didn't look possible. Looking back always makes things work as second guesses. Not factoring in your current location shows you just how stupid you were when what you really need to know is just how smart you are now. We were stranded, unable to go back or forward: at the point of every human being in each moment of life. Stuck. My body knew it and my head amplified it: does that sound familiar, like something you try to avoid? But along with this came a presence I had seldom experienced, everything seemed more real. Pictures of great tragedy ran in my head. I saw blood, my body crumbled on the rocks, death, dismemberment and I think the Hindenburg. I wouldn't be writing this if we hadn't made it down. We did but I remember that day to this in the same way I remember the time my brother and I were in a cave in the middle of nowhere and I got stuck and panicked. Those were the good old days.

Think of the worst things that have ever happened in your life. Think of the worst fear, trauma and terror. That is what your life is like each moment: honest. Every moment you are keeping these emotions at bay. You are warding them off by being more superficial, less observant and to some degree numb and dumb.

You wander through life finding excuses for the occasional blips on the screen from your depths. It doesn't have to be this way. Your only incentive for going deep is to hide; it should be to seek. When the fear or terror shows up you can go under it rather than trying to build something else on top of it. You can face it, smile at it, shed a tear for it and move into it. Under the worst is always something much better than anything you can think of. Under the worst is way better than best.

You won't get anywhere as you continue to sidestep. Dancing can be a form of seduction but it, of itself, doesn't really get you anywhere. To get anywhere, like where you are, you will have to move forward in spite of great evidence that there is danger ahead. You will have to stay perfectly still in spite of great evidence that there is danger coming your way and you will have to learn to run away from anywhere that isn't real enough to threaten you. The gingerbread smell wafts from the beautiful little cabin, potentially a crematorium.

Spiritual Seduction

There are a few steps necessary to not get anywhere. One is you will have to release content. You will have to stop blaming something else as a surrogate, superficial pain for the much more real pain deeper within you. Everybody has been abused, everybody has suffered and everybody has had too much pain to carry in the moment. You have been abandoned but that can't keep you from getting into Heaven unless you use it as an excuse to not open next time. You have been hurt but you won't get hurt any worse if you admit the pain, find the pleasure in it too, and continue to open.

You are jealous of someone. You aren't really jealous, you just had a moment in which you performed three simple steps of abuse: You considered that whoever you are jealous of isn't you (which is a lie), you then liked them (their location, intelligence, dress, wit, or something) better than you liked your own, and then came the cherry, you decided that it would always be this way. These three steps go on anytime you are jealous. Other steps go on for every emotion. The steps have some elements in common but what they all have in common is that they are all bullshit. They are bullshit because they are something that you are willing to look at that is a patch, a throw rug, over something that you aren't willing to look at.

These patches hold in infection but block vision. They seem to restrict pain to a certain avenue rather than admitting the general offense that is all around you. You have performed magic; a specific distortion has become the excuse for a general offense. The false cure: A specific remedy for a general malady. You can waste your life here on Earth trying to solve metaphorical problems, logistical daymares. You can suffer with an object which seems easier than suffering without one. It isn't easier. It is time to stop lying and start experiencing the sensations that are everywhere. When you open you will have many sensations: a balance of wonderful ones and not so wonderful ones. You will suffer and celebrate independent of content. You will flow, get blocked and flow again.

All of this is part of putting on the brakes. It seems it is about letting go but it isn't. It is about ending general braking so that you can brake specifically. Anytime you are braking for more than fifteen seconds you alter, downward, your opinion of the general performance of the vehicle. In other words: The status quo is negotiable downward so fast that it would make you dizzy if it didn't have you so busy thinking you are good that you don't notice that when you are pissing away the downside you are pissing away the upside too.

You have to learn where the gas is and where the brakes are. You have to get that foot off the brakes and be ready both on the breaks and the gas. It is you who control the speed of your life. The only two direct influences you can have on your life are that you can influence your speed and your disposition. The relationship between these two is called inspiration.

Rid yourself of content, rid yourself of low self-esteem and you will finally be able to really jam on the brakes, so you will really be able to get going too.

Candy corn is good for putting on the brakes, so is sex. A really, really good stinky foreign cheese works too. Other things will speed you up: like time around wonderful, fast people, sex, very light food, walking in the woods, dipping in cold water, learning new things, listening to Beethoven, being tickled gently for hours, praying to an image of yourself, talking when you don't want to, being as stupid as you can in the company of people you want to show off to, setting up a booth and painting caricatures for ten dollars each if you can't paint at all, singing out loud, calling somebody famous on the phone and reaching them, adopting a grandmother or two, giving away your pets, doing something that isn't compatible with anything you have ever done before, stopping short during sex and making certain that you don't orgasm on purpose, having sex if you normally don't have any, writing a love letter to someone who you have forgotten that you love but still do and replacing a very old habit with a newer one (this even works for nuns).

Speaking of nuns: We had a former nun in a course recently. She is well into her seventies. On the second day of the course participants went to a nudist park. The look on her face when she got back home from a naked day among strangers had me remember that everybody is nude under their clothes and in the eyes of the Lord and they just don't remember it often enough.

If you want to slow down all you need to do is think more. All you need to do is make up a story and believe it. All you need to do is move away from something that you really want to move away from. All you need to do is hold to your habits as though they are life or death. All you need to do to slow up is have a cup of coffee or put your child on Ritalin. All you need to do to slow up is take acid, marijuana or Prozac. All you need to do to slow down is listen to Madonna, do some therapy, read a best seller or watch TV. All you need to do to slow down is ignore art and count your possessions often. All you need to do to slow down is stay busy and talk about how much you have to do. All you have to do to slow down is have a drink of alcohol or spend time with family members who have not updated their imaginings about who you are. All you need to do to slow down is just do anything that isn't in your best interest.

All you need to do to speed up is to meditate, not go to Sedona, give away something you really like to somebody you don't like. All you need to do to speed up is FLIRT, FLIRT and FLIRT some more. All you need to do to speed up is to let go. All you need to do to slow up is to hold on. All you need to do to speed up is to spend time with me. All you need to do to slow down is go back to school or back to your mother. All you need to do to slow up is say that you don't have enough time or enough money but that you really do want to do it if only you could. All you need to do to speed up is to learn the unthinkable. All you need to do to slow up is to make a big deal about Christmas, unless you are Muslim, then making a big deal about Christmas works. All you have to do to slow down is think that this isn't it or that your life is getting better. All you need to do to slow down is think that people get somehow worse as they age. All you need to do to slow down is embrace apathy. All you need to do to speed up is to open when you want to close and close when you want to open. All you need to do to open up is to fire an old friend and find a new one who is much more challenging.

I could go on but I think you get the point. There are many ways to speed up and slow down. You really don't have to worry about going too fast for too long because you can always visit the stupid bush, pick some fruit and eat it. None of the above speeding up and slowing down suggestions are universally true, some are more generally applicable than others. Dipping in cold water almost always gives people a little jolt of being awake, while performing according to culture's dictates, Backstreet Boys, coffee or beanie babies almost never do.

While none of the suggestions above are spiritual there are specific connections between life on Earth and the seduction of life on Earth all the way to spirit. Any real yes is from the spirit world. It has no opposite, it is not a yes to anything in particular, it is a complete and perfect yes, yes, yes. Any no has a basis in the corporal world. Every no gets infected, every no has you end up with a fever and a full complement of problems that result from it. Seduction is the conversion of a worldly no to a worldly yes. Spiritual seduction is the conversion of anything worldly to a spiritual yes. You are a spiritual creature, though it is often hard for you to tell that moment to moment. You are obvious to me. I see you. I see the spiritual you. I hear your, yes and the spiritual yes is always resounding. I hear it, I see it, I feel it from here from there. It is there, it is waiting and it never gets tired of waiting but it is also not allergic to the sun. It can and will come out in the open. When it does so you will understand how good life is. You will understand that within the simple things are the complex. You will see the perfection in others and you will hurt for them: hurt badly and deeply. You will see yourself as God sees you and know with complete wisdom why God leaves us alone. We already have it, we are in the way of our seeing it, feeling it, smelling it, tasting it and particularly hearing it. This world is not a construct, nor will it bow to any. This world is not ours, it is us. On a spiritual plain this is your world; on an earthly plane it is always a struggle, too small seats, lousy food and a destination that makes no difference when you get there.

Muster your spirituality, seduce Earth into letting you go. This book is a ticket for you. There are many tickets but one....

APPENDIX 1

REALLY SEDUCTION — A FEW WORDS ABOUT WORDS

"I like having her here." For every sentence there is a standard complement, this is the trailer, to carry baggage, that nearly every unenlightened American person adds to a phrase. Do you know what the standard complement is?

The standard complement is always some version of the other side of the coin, it is something like what would go on the other side of the scale to balance off what has just been said in an erstwhile, unsuccessful attempt to reinforce through movement in the other direction.

The standard complement of, "I like having her here," is "better than not having her here." That isn't, of course, what I meant at all. I was in no way implying anything about not having her here. "Having her here" has "not having her here" enter your head equally which is why even when she is here she isn't really here for you. The unenlightened interpretation is to like having her here and to like not having her here to the exact same degree, relieving her of being here or even being in the process of relieving her of the oppression of pretending that she is something other than light.

Sub-standard complement—pessimism. Super-standard complement is a thinking interpretation based primarily on the words themselves, "How nice, for you, that you like having her here." Every sentence has one standard complement; this is the fabric of culture and an infinite number of sub and super complements, this is the stuff of depression and politics respectively, not respectfully. It also has, and this is where spirituality comes in because it allows you to explore every nook and cranny of what seems so much to be here, a neutral complement which sheds light on something by the nonpreferential exploration of meaningless connections to other previously unobserved similarities and differences, the observation of which increases the size that one must admit one is without having a backfire of pride. This is the Ericsonian approach to cyclotherapy. Cyclotherapy is the study of patterns not directly but by lateral movement through what isn't revealing that it isn't. In other words, storytelling with a purpose.

There are metafours and metaphives. Metaphor is a story which shows the connections between two similar things and metaphives are stories which show the connections between two similar things, the contents of one of the things being sufficiently personal that one derives insights otherwise unattainable about one's own predicament by a specific generalization of a skilled laser generalizer, said cyclotherapist.

I used to play kick the can when I was a kid. Memories of a silver swing set and it getting dark and running a lot and liking being "not it" and not liking being "it." But I also remember years later being at the ice skating rink and thinking that everybody was rather impressed with me and playing pom, pom pool away, with one person in the middle who is "it" and the rest going from side to side becoming it by degrees and I always wanted to be "it" and always wanted "not to be it" because either was OK with me. And I think that the lesson here is in the first case with kick the can, it just seemed that no matter how good I was, I wasn't good enough unless I "wasn't it," making the whole game a little of "this isn't it." But by the time I hit the ice I was sufficiently good that another connection with other skaters and the very process of skating took precedence making me more or less the same and allowing me to win no matter what happened. Other than the one time that I bumped my head and had to go to the hospital because that time I can't remember winning because I was out in the cold and can't remember anything at all. And I am sure that I won that time too. Life is supposed to start out big, get way too small and then at some point cross the border of just right. Where are you? I'm it, you're it too.

Every coin that has two sides has two sides, every phrase that is spoken has many sides but two which are in the greatest opposition to each other. If you can make one of the ones with the greatest opposition you; immediately, you have an ally, but you also have the opposition. If you make one of the billions of ones with less opposition you, you will learn less and have less support than from the greatest opposition: GO phrase. The greater the opposition, if you are successful in expression, the greater your strength and less your tension from dealing with the expression. Stress fractures the expression, as a writer or a speaker of the English language, you just have to get these things out of your head. Ignoring standard, super and sub complements has you not able to evangelize about how good or bad things are except in readily rejectable doses which has you, in effect, not be able to get rid of them at all.

As you raise your tolerance for GO, sufficiently extreme opposition, you will be able to move freely between any two thighs with yourself being the human bridge and this is the use of consciousness that I would prefer if it weren't that the very preferences that we have are exactly what get in the way of our perceiving connections.

A FEW WORDS ABOUT COMPARISON

Complement presupposes relationship, comparison, sneakily, does too but it does so in a pejorative competitive manner.

Watch: "It isn't like it used to be." Or, "I used to think that too." Or, "What would be the purpose of that?" or, "Yes, I know what you mean." Each of these expressions contains the superiority of the speaker over the listener. In doing so there is a kind of revealing of competition and the completion of competition all in the same allegedly complete thought. While these are too subtle to learn about in logic class, they are also too subtle to get noticed in everyday speech, but anything that you lose just slowly enough you don't notice that you lose at all.

Most people are in a battle for any esteem that can be found. Most people think that if they push you down a little they raise themselves a lot. This sort of linear comparison just has to die. At its basest it just implies too much, insinuates too much and gives too little. You won't find these in this book, at least not accidentally. What I want you to know more than anything else is that we are in the same boat and that sometimes you know we are and sometimes I know we are and sometimes in those moments of shared orgasm we both know we are. And I am not talking about sex here. If I can compliment you without complementing myself, then I have to be careful but I can have a lot of fun. It is a little like getting a small box as a child and discovering that in it there is a vinyl mess that when blown up, puffed into aggressively, turns into a rather big dinosaur or clown or cartoon character that with one's small eyes at least three takes are required to include it. The more takes it takes, the more interesting it is and the more opportunity there is for faith and trust in the process and the more it forces sample rate to increase and attention span to lengthen. If you can get puffed up enough you will get perspective just looking at how many places you show up that you didn't think you were and how the view is from way the heck up there.

You don't need to be brought down to size, you need to get sufficiently big sufficiently rapidly that you don't know what things are right now but you know that they are bigger and potentially more wonderful, like Alice, and more threatening, like everybody else than you imagined possible.

In short I want you to yes yourself and spread that yes around to include everything else so that this is your universe and welcome to it. While saying this doesn't do it, the unconventions in much of the text of this book and the invitation to make of these anything you do in the process of making them what you don't expands you. When you meet a word you hadn't expected your first tendency is to question yourself but the second is to blame the writer. The first lasts such a short time and the second, though short-lived too, almost always lasts at least five times longer, forcing your attention outside yourself for resolution when the real resolution must happen within. I figure, and oddly it turns out this way, that if you get enough chances to make sense of something that doesn't you discover yourself between all things that seem otherwise un related. This tops synchronicity in that synchronicity is like the odd rocky path across the stream and this is like the stream itself.

It is odd to travel by river. It is odd in that you are always flowing and you are perpetually seeing sights that only the river seas. While it is unsettling at first it is later, of course, the only way to go. Crossing the river just doesn't teach you the same thing that going with it does. Crossing it shows your ability to go against the odds and to cut, sideways, on your way at least to proving you can make it. Flowing with it presents trust and surrender and it also, if done well, allows you to relax, in fact, demands that relaxation. Just let it flow, your self-esteem will be taken care of in the process, you will think faster so you are bound to think better of yourself. You will also see the terrain in the way that water does and you were meant to and you can redefine fun as too easy and too revealing in the process. I know it seems easier to define yourself by competition but that really isn't easy or natural at all, it just is typical of the iceberg and can sink even the biggest of ships. Let the phrases stand on their own in you, let them put themselves together and let double and triple meanings raise your wits and wisdom as you discover that you do naturally yes your way to this big You party.

APPENDIX 2

SPILLAGE

There are bound to be things that just don't make it into the more regular parts of a book like this. Here are some of many quotes that either didn't get into the text or I don't remember getting into the text. Either way enjoy!

*****

If you are going to get more intelligent you have to raise the ceiling of the stupidity you are willing to go through, especially in the presence of others who see it clearly, for that is the hardest kind. You even have to expand your (t)error to the degree that it encompasses all that you used to think was intelligent and converts it to stupidity: this is the alchemy of intelligence.

Less and less off becomes more and more off becomes further and further off as one speeds up. Einstein again.

Sometimes it takes people a while to puff up to the point of downfall. The faster the better as with most things other than naps and napes.

I need you to love me more than you love your patterns, hate me more than you hate your patterns, see me more than you see your patterns. Love me more than you hate your patterns, and hate me more than you love your patterns. Indifference I cannot deal with. Indifference is the failure to make the distinctions that give one a truly three-dimensional playground.

Same movie different content.

Spiritual Seduction

He's coming back. He's coming, back. The difference is one comma, coma, and from religion to pornography or optimism.

Someday after I'm here something will come up or intervene and after I'm gone will perhaps be the warning on the lips of the masses as with Jesus.

I think Olympic sprinters should have to hold hands (while running). They are always running and this way there would be many more photo finishes winning by a nose.

You need to measure the clarity of the sky you will tolerate. This will tell you a lot about your patterns. I seem to be committed to at least one little cloud in my sky, it seems to put my vastness in just the perfect perspective.

When I was little I thought everything was allright. Those were the good old days. Now I am bigger and everything is allright. That converts the past to foreshadowing and makes these the good new days.

If there is any consistency in life maybe the future is young enough or old enough to know better when she sees it. I dance on my 194-foot sloop, full nine sails to the wind, she can do eight knots in dead calm, even faster when the sun is out. I call her the future.

You can't get hurt here, think of your past. You can't get hurt here, but you sure can think you did for a lifetime. Ouch.

Thinking you lost it is much worse than losing it. This is when your simulation exceeds the reality of reality which is the correct use of illusion. It is also the demand for the antidote called orgasm. Thinking is the highest form the mind takes, specifically thinking as embellishment of reality.

Thinking—means walking through the problematic swamps in your mind. Lowlands are nearly anytime that you didn't see things as they were.
Thickening—means what you do to yourself when you do too much thinking, it is making yourself sick by spending too much time in the swamps of your mind.

I was wrong about everything: that is how hard it is to surrender, even internal inconsistency has been activated to get in your way. Let me explain: Hearing that you were wrong about everything, your partner does one of two things. Either he celebrates how wonderful it is to win or polarity sets in and he begins to argue that isn't certainly true. If it is your real partner, your own intellect maybe, it notices that if you were wrong about everything, you are wrong about the statement that you were wrong about everything so it doesn't really shed much light on how right or wrong you are. And, the sum write and wrongness of two people doesn't add up to one hundred percent, it adds up to 200 percent, one is not only not really related to the other but not certainly the complement that couples tend to think is the case when they are arguing with the one they love to produce a result they won't be able to stand when the time to be alone comes.

The upside always requires one more turn, the turn not taken. It takes a lack of effort at the precise moment one is tempted to make it, which allows centripetal force magic to make the universe your ally, circling you around rather than careening off into diversion. The possibility: New pivotal points become an open trapless door begging for vertical movement toward self.

Content resort—people go there for vacation when their process doesn't vary sufficiently.

Try and stay away from logistical, or otherwise, daymares. These are those bitchy four-legged creatures that show up and are enough to ruin an otherwise good day. They do this by reminding you that there is something that you have forgotten the memory of which casts a shadow sufficiently long to darken Mother Theresa's whole life.

A sharp knife is the happiest when cutting. If not slicing for too long it questions its purpose. Even longer and it questions its existence, even longer and it becomes a dull, reduced self-esteem human being. This isn't the way evolution should really work.

Dating should be the third highest form of evolution on Earth. The second should be reproduction and the first ascension.

How would you like a lifetime of revelation in a week? In other words: How would you like 100 years of revelations in a week? If we are to extend our lifetimes, we will have to expand the pleasure and perception of possibility each moment. There is a much too deniable relationship between extension and expansion.

Coincidentally and almost causally, there is so much almost causally it is the root of all temptations.

You have to be pretty well-backed into a corner to be interested in progress. In other words: The present has to suck for your interest to leave it for the unknown. When this parting is for fun then adventure ensues. When this parting is defensive worry ensues. It is the difference between leaving freely or being thrown out. Dealing with the future is all the more different given your allergy to change. Ha, ha, ha, choo?

I want my own personal Lost and Found.

We are building to a climax which won't be the climax. When articles can be differentiated you are making useful distinctions and progress is just around the next coroner. Death is the best way I know to ensure that you will get what you don't already have and don't want to.

My interest in women tried to go out with garters but I was so young and didn't know what I was talking about still. If you are young enough to have unhooked a garter or two in the heat of passion you are old enough to know better than nearly everything. Then, it is time for anachronistic existence or a new pair of dimes.

"This is Not Humanly Possible" sign on the door of the Everyday Spiritual Path. The absence of upset on the spiritual path is eerie and enough to piss you off. When you think it is theoretical, think again. Two no's do make a right.

Today on Divorce Court: Adam and Eve: The Settlement. I was rather shocked, after all these years I could have been going to therapy, that there is something called root stock. What root stock is is the roots of apple trees. Once these roots are there any type of apple can be grafted on the obvious part of the tree and will produce. You can even graft more than one type of apple on the same tree. You can't do much about how far from the tree the apple falls but you can do a lot about what kind of apple falls. This, to me, means that our history really doesn't have to predict our present and certainly doesn't need to be carried forward to the future. This idea, though on a first name basis with truth, doesn't find any friends in the therapist's office.

If you don't trust me when I tell you something, you will have to check. What use am I to you then? What good are you? The purpose of a check is to modify a raise giving it more power. If you check all night and then raise, the bluff is nearly perfect. People notice the unordinary more than the ordinary. They pay more for the ordinary.

You don't get do-overs in life, or, and this is much more relevant, in death. Reincarnation is a lifesaver without much flavor, it is two halves hope, one half worry and three halves frustration. A friend of mine, well, a neighbor, when I was in high school smoked though he wasn't addicted yet. He just thought it was cool, once he was old enough to play with matches, and didn't notice it was a way of getting burned.

In relationship you have only one thing to forgive them for. You have to forgive them for levels on which they don't care. You will find these if you have the courage to look for them. The best way to look for them is to act sufficiently outside the norm that they show up naturally. That way you can learn many things as you are waiting for them to show up. If you can't have fun in the waiting room, for anything, you can't really have fun. If you end up waiting you don't end up happy.

Spiritually speaking, as you progress you will go through valleys where you know knowbody. At these times your mind is your only consolation.

Disseminating your problems more widely or with more or less vehemence than your solutions smudges your future memories. It stops you from generating what you want then, now.

With this kind of open heart it isn't mathematical; 1 equals 1.345 million or so it seems.

If you want to break the leash, "the ties that bind" from proverbs, don't make your run from full extension, slack is your friend in a case like this.

Women usually don't get mad when they get screwed, but when it stops.

So many "nows" so little time.

There is wisdom in the orgasm available nowhere else. Wilhelm Reich knew that long before they burned his books.

I am the winner of the lottery whether I am the winner in fact, partially because I already know the number and the rest because I don't. If you understand this, "God bless you." If you have someone explain it to you, "Double God bless you." Double because you have found someone and are able to listen to them. If you just don't get it, date a few more people who might understand, then untry abstinence.

Writing down is easy, and condescending. Writing up, nobody likes a tattle tale, Heaven only knows that.

As The Three Stooges said on their way to the (candy) bar in an atypically spiritual moment, "None for all and all for none."

You don't get do-overs in life so this book isn't very edited.

How much time each day do you spend consciously defining yourself, how much time unconsciously defending? These two make up the hole of most people's day. How much time do you spend really defining yourself?

Early yeses are easy for a stuck person to give since they ride on an unwavering sea of no.

You, in mint condition, a collector's item, not a collector. You are the head of the "too easy piggy bank fame" and the receptacle for the human currency, attention. And who is that? That person next to you in bed.

There is a knock at the door, anything that comes along has arrived, at last. It should be met at the door not by anticipation but by flexibility.

With enough common sense you can close your own "I's." Now that is the great American tragedy.

You can't take any insecurities you aren't willing to lose into relationship and expect it to work unless you thrive on disappointment. Your no's have to be like water. "When do I get attention?" is a metaphor for no.

You can't breathe through your no's unless you wake up. Your no's suffocate you, they should humor you.

Surrender without respect always bites hard later.

You see all of you reflected in me—you have a preference for seeing only part of you, the rest you blame me for. It is usually the upside in a mask that you blame me for.

At some point you will have to admit that you were wrong in equal measure to your right otherwise you are doomed not to learn.

Playboy is pornographic from either side of the jail house bars. From one side it is too revealing; and from the other side, the free side, it shows too much without enough experience involved. It blushes in the face of the former and pales in the face of the ladder. You will need the ladder to get out. Until then should you like that kind of wishful pornography, you reveal that you aren't really on either side but as stuck, well anchored and going nowhere as the bars themselves.

Auditory and Visual are phenomena of the mind, Kinesthetic is a function of the body.

We need more creative tautologies like: The rose is a budding artist.

Spirituality will insure you and the walls you will surely hit finding yourself.

If the best day of your life isn't the worst day of your life it will be short-lived and you will be too.

What if we really had an open school—just a really big room and people and nothing else? What would naturally evolve, showing us unnatural is what we have? What sales would have to be made? What links to the community shown? What use of the public library? Wouldn't there be a lot of show and tell? Wouldn't the whole thing more accurately mirror what we really need in our community and wouldn't it get to the point, oddly enough, that the people who excelled would be both a larger and much more coordinated group than is the case now?

Purely visual criteria for a spouse can work, but install a dimmer in your bedroom for aging purposes.

Another woman is an aphrodisiac for both partners.

Practicality is about proportions, you need to find out what equals what.

What culture offers as acceptable and good, retards spiritual perception and precludes spiritual progress. Perception should precede progress or fear ensues.

Everyone has a specialty, the viewing of which from a removed position looks both excessive and excessively wonderful, this it truly the not gross national product of the United States.

Reading the future in the present is the second closest to safe you will get, the closest is the vulnerability of present from present.

To find out who someone thinks he or she is look closely at them. To find out who they really think they are, look a few levels away at who they pick to "romance" with.

Don't let details get in your way—clean'em up.

If you aren't willing to cut teeth at any age you won't be a sufficiently eager beaver to have much other than bare bones existence with a few baubles to gnaw on.

A good woman isn't satisfied until she has everything. There are no bad women. It is a concession and polite of women to let men walk around generally taller.

The extrapolation of overlooking discomfort is death with great pain, a not-nearly-short-enough stop on the way.

My data is based enough in science that there is room for art. So you can use my data to calibrate your tests. This means that I have arrived and am not going anywhere.

Most of you had the ever-loving shit beaten out of you before the hind end of the first quarter.

You can dance to a swan song and when you do you live.

The mother is f—king without admitting she is f—king around. The daughter is f—king around without admitting that she is f—king.

Flirting isn't real butt, it can backfire just like the real thing, accidentally and obviously resulting in pregnancy of the worst kind: unnoticed.

I'll be your one and lonely tonight.

She takes the third when I catch her with an enlisted man.

She takes the thirteenth when I ask her to take out the garbage.

I have so many people around me bleating ignorance.

Downloading personal data—having sex without losing anything in the process.
By the bye—not leaving alone.
Buy the bye—insecurity at dusk.
By the buy—waiting in line.

When the husband kills himself at the wife's place of business it might be safe to assume he had a communication to deliver.

Everybody is as accurate as their stories will let them be.

If you like where you err your relating stands a chance.

The IRS distinguishes between an accident and criminal behavior by the presence of a pattern. If there is a pattern it is criminal, or a misunderstanding. The more benefit inures to the person, the stronger must be the argument for accident or misunderstanding.

If this same logic applies to people's everyday life, things get interesting. Listen to people's stories, watch their patterns, see what they miss and you too can be an honorary auditor. Do this enough with others and you will be ready to see yourself.

Compulsive people are always lazy, too lazy to be present.

Drug—anything bought without being sold.

Talking is always pushing.

Marriage—let freedom ring.

Wisdumb.

People who speak of God and country never keep those two in order.

All content is substance and all substance offers the probability, if not the actuality, of substance abuse. They are all addicted to something.

Is there a correlation between life and wealth?

You need an antiagonal drug to be taken in case of agony.

Technology is a surrogate for sufficiently intelligent people. The real purpose of technology is to speed us up in the presence of others and to take apart our operating system by revealing the always inherent flaw in having one. Being a UNIX doesn't end the need for relationship crashes to learn, and having the best operating system doesn't always result in Darwinian speed.

I wish I had been there when we broke up. She did it in her own head without me. It would have been harder to do in my presence, under the pressure of the universe I look pretty good. Under the pressure of her illusion she doesn't do too well.

If you forget what someone is for you will soon be against your own best interest.

You are always jeopardizing who you aren't. Who you are jeopardizes it the least because it never calls and never writes.

If you speak to crazy people as though they are sane you become one, sometimes two.

Schools mistakenly reward accuracy not willingness.

It takes different patterns to fulfill needs than to fulfill wants. If you don't know this you will convert by constants increasing your buying, but not your power in the process.

Work should be the dessert while life is the main course. Every business is lying to their employees and then indignant when their employees lie back.

Spiritual Seduction

A man can love a woman he knows in one way and a woman he doesn't in quite another. There is little overlay between the two. Women don't have the ability to understand this as they take even math personally. Women can like two people in different ways but can only love the same.

Never be around someone it isn't dangerous to underestimate.

People who are too identified with something that isn't them say, "I don't care" when they try and let go. People with much more perspective say, "It doesn't matter."

Blessing—to be a target and not in control.
Tragedy—to be on target and think you are in control.

Enough common sense will close your own "I's."

Flexibility not anticipation or anxiety makes a good mater dee.

Money is a bad ghostly homeopathic for self-esteem.

A broken heart is one of the only useful ways around math.

If generalization requires effort it is pre-mature. If learning doesn't begin with observation it is rote at best.

There are no parts of her we won't be able to use. Translation: She isn't very interesting. There is always a nicer way to get some point across that says more about them, to them, and less about you.

Try and stray away from logistical daymares.

Thinking you lost it is so much worse than losing it. This is when your simulation of reality exceeds reality which is the correct use of illusion but can be easily mistaken for personal growth.

I think Olympic sprinters should have to hold hands, while running, that way we might be able to run with them. Another way is that they could marry my ex-wife or your ex-husband.

Your arm will get very tired if it is raining outside and you have an umbrella, and it is open, and you hold the umbrella out so far that you are all wet, but there is some lesson to be learned here.

If you can find a teenager's button, you are one.

I need you to love me more than you love your patterns, hate me more than you hate your patterns and notice your patterns more than you notice me.

Women must always perceive that they are included; men must always perceive that they are exempt. These are for something like optimal performance.

It would be neat to have some semblance of correlation between stimulus and response.

You need to think the undoable, do the unthinkable and lose your rear view mirror. Especially if you support others in suffering from the over-ample persistence of your too thought out "but."

It is easier to con fuse opposites than anything in between. A true believer,, an endangering, inquisitional species, converts for content and is easier to vary, wary, than process.

If there is even the thinnest glimpse of pretense, it absolutely obscures the absolute.

If you put on a show for someone you won't really want them around much. It is too difficult and time wasting to put on a show for long.

The loss of the loves of your life are the price you pay for not loving everything.

I don't want to go off the deep end about swimming. I don't want to go off half-cocked about hunting or mating.

Pick your friends carefully you little thinker you, for it is only among smaller thinkers you can look big or bigger or biggest and not undertake the apple cart upsetting task of learning. If you really hate learning make sure you spend time with people who revere you. Begging for self-knowledge pre-empts it.

She thinks highly of herself and has low self-esteem, yes, there will be a battle here today. Yes, she will not have enough attention left for you, for it is the ongoing dance between low (self-esteem), which is deep, and high opinions, which are much more shallow, which stops her from anything other than defending her from herself and stops you, in you, from moving on.

Unless of course you are attracted to everyone, then you best pray.

There are secrets and there are withholds. Until you can tell, out loud, the difference between the two, you aren't really ready for relating.

It is time to die—I am not talking a literal death but the birth of literal in your "life."

George Bush, in an attempt at honesty, is moving the intelligence department out of the White House, maybe even out of Washing town. JFK had a passion for the secret service. Gerald Ford had a passion for things that go bump, his head, in the night. Bill Clinton was the head of state. I wonder how soon during his presidency Reagan forgot he was President.

There need be no economy of emotion.

I have a major in psychology and a minor in agoraphobia. I got my degrees, necessarily, through the mail.

Youth in Asia.

It is important to take your deepest romantic conversations off time-delay. What do you get when you mix the technology of time-delay with reincarnation? Hope or Marcel Marceau.

I am just so happy I can't figure out what to not do next.

APPENDIX 3[1]

BROKEN HEART MEMOIRS

If you are going to play you are going to have your heart broken. You are going to have it handed to you on a platter with a look, on the part of another, which indicates some combination of "what did you expect?" and "there you go sweetie." Your mother tried to like you all the time, how did that turn out? Heartbreak is always better than putting on the brakes. When you put on the brakes you stop prematurely not hitting the pain of the wall, just getting the pain. You need to hit the wall, you need to crash and maybe burn, because, until you get sufficiently subtle that is the only way you can die. Most people don't hit the wall, they don't know how to push themselves sufficiently to get up the speed to even make it to the wall. You just wouldn't want to ride in a vehicle that wasn't wall tested. You wouldn't want to mountain climb with someone who didn't even consider falling possible but you wouldn't want to climb with someone who considered falling all the time either. The wall teaches you in a non-negotiable way. Early on, without subtlety, this is the way you have to learn. The unit of measure of relationship is heartbreaks per minute.

You can't rise above it, it hurts. You told her everything you always wanted to say to someone. You mustered your hot dog,

[1] You can't tell who I am from my heart anymore. You can from my appendix because in my appendix you find what I couldn't process, what I couldn't utilize, what the mainstream wouldn't find digestible.

courage, with strongest mustard available. She translates you into her world and blames you for hurting her. Ouch. You give him everything you have and you see him thinking about someone else. Double ouch. There are degrees of ouch but all of them have to do with inaccurate translation, insufficient exchange rate, undeliverable communication or restricted flow. At the base of every broken heart is a yes or no that should have been given but wasn't. Neither a yes nor a no can break a heart, because at their base is a commitment. Commitment should beget a commitment not a diversion. Commitment should beget equal commitment or it hurts. If boldly enough given it leads to learning; if timidly given it leads to regrets. Learning leads to a better future while regrets fester into resignation which is excessive justification and the cessation of even peace as possibility. Diversion is a lateral change of subject in the face of an invitation to duolateral commitment. When the diversion isn't even recognized as such then there seems to be no possible Amens, amends.

Your track record at hide and seek is second to none and then you meet someone and you find out that your track record is second to one. It is hard to hear that you have finished after some fact the person is holding more dearly than they are holding you.

Who would have considered a sensitivity hidden so well, so deep, so far below the water line? It helps to remember that you are mostly water, except when hide tide hits unexpectedly in the middle of "the dark night of the soul." Nothing seems to matter in this moment of discovery, when you discover that your "dark night of the soul" doesn't even show up on their radar. Ouch to the third, or next.

Warning: The ones who seem to care the most, right out of the box without some complementary commitment from you, legal or just self-made therapists, will dash you later when you least expect it and you will find yourself way down and way out with the huge temptation to blame them, which is the problem, because it precludes you from learning if you attribute the cause outside yourself.

Most of time you don't know you have a heart or could give it. Is it really healthy to find out so quickly that it is there? "Yes." Could you possibly live from it and temper those moments when it won't be denied even by the greatest rational attempts in the world? "Yes." Would you want to? "Yes." That way you would have to be in love all the time. You would have to play until somebody turns the porch light on for you to come in and then you would have to come in all at once, from the cold or otherwise. In other words: Where the heart is concerned you are where you are, you are who you are, and you are serving a term of life without parole. Certainly anything less is a death sentence, but broken hearts hurt. It's an old fashioned anachronism, this staying out so late after notice has been given to retreat. It is better to have played forever than never to have played at all.

Breaking your heart on Earth prepares you for spirituality. It is the rinsing, cutting and preparing of the vegetables prior to the meal. You are welcome at God's table, but this isn't potluck and you aren't getting any younger, you can't get there without being on the menu first. Appealing to God's culinary whims is the spiritual equivalent of trying to have relationship work on Earth. God loves jazz. Recklessness must be done quickly or you can be brought up on charges of premedicated recklessness: pre dick table ity. If you didn't see the broken heart coming then it really has nothing to do with you. You take a few Alka Seltzers, or aspirin and go to bed for a while and it seems better. But if you saw it coming right from the start, if you welcomed it in knowing well that it would break anything you currently perceive yourself to be, then you are either a glutton, yourself, for punishment or you are almost done with this worldly play and ready for spirituality. Earth never offers what it seems to, spirituality always doesn't either but Earth always offers less. Seeing it coming is an important part of welcoming it in. Don't worry, you won't ever be ready, but you can be happy, and you can't be both. Have you ever seen a survivalist with a genuine smile? Like a lucky adolescent finally learning that it is the least resourceful person who often assumes authority, the tears fall. It is the one willing to dash the hopes who seems to be calling the shots. One can attend to the tears but it might be more useful to notice how far they fall or whether they are red or not.[2] Trace tears gravity aided trajectory back to the well of the soul where all hearts are one and you will discover that it is leased and that someone else is the rightful owner.

I dreamed of another. Of watching but knowing better than to open. Of being caught by someone slower than I am, but with one endearing trait a heart not a finger could be put on. Or, what has happened to love? The kind without opposite. The kind without object. The kind that there never used to be but in the squeaky clean memories of the amnesiac widow long after the event in which widowhood was first conceived.

Nothing happened to it, it is here, it is well, it is as quietly requited as it can be, which is not much when you are preoccupied and too much when you are not. Like the first little gasp of conscious morning breath, or crocus in spring, and only a constant reminder of life's variability throughout the day.

On a high wire it is easy and obvious what one is risking. But there are so many low wires and no wires that the false sense of security incompatible with life itself seems to have been elected without a vote. If your heart breaks you want a recount. A recount of emotions ignored, of sensations felt but never found out. You want a recount of available bodies and seemingly

---

[2] Spiritual tears are red. Earthly tears are clear.

unavailable touches and touchés. You want thoughts thrown out during the count because they don't. You can't know where you stand in love. Try as you do. The balance of might and do come to a premature ending, without your resolution and with theirs.

If the race is to find out who can be the most hopeless romantic then it isn't really worth it. If the race, instead, is to find who can open, who can donate the most blood to the lack of cause in the face of fear, then you have a race worth running, if it never ends. If you are dependent on the end, knowing, then you can't enjoy the running, hugging or kissing. A dead martyr gathers no moss. You need to be a mortal loving a mortal. Then a mortal loving an immortal. Jesus may have died for your sins but you need to learn to live with them. It is easier to die for something than to live for something. Living gets in the way of dying so often you almost become conwinced, (*v.* 1. the facial expression of knowing you are going to be hit before you are 2. being taken in by such an expression so much so that you don't deliver the desired blow).

Your pain is as close as you get to the present. It reminds you there is a heart there, a stomach there and behind all that organ music a person. You. Earthly love is supposed to find that person. It hurts good the first time. It hurts when mixed with a certain amount of innocence, of, "it shouldn't have happened." The second time is jaded because you should have known better. If you never know better and continue to open then you are dipping your toe in spirituality. Angel toes, light on your feet, leading the way leaping from broken heart to inside yourself.[3]

There is a big difference between throwing stones and building the pyramids. I know you don't want to be me but I do want to be you. My heart cracks open and spills its contents, something the mind is perpetually encouraging, superficially, the mind to do.

If your dog bites someone and has never shown signs of doing so before that is a surprise, blood and an accident. But that innocence can't be reclaimed. The dog cannot be a non-biter. From that moment on anytime the dog doesn't bite it is a surprise. The once-bitten sometimes forgets last, sometimes first, often denial, always denial. Remembered exactly is the eloquent door of the present, glowing, she entered and remained, finally she left in a doggy bag, all dog-eared. Remembered more hazily is the absence of learning: a future which looks enough like the past to demand a lack of attention. Remembered not at all is the rapid, blemished, recklessness of youth.

If you are a puzzle manufacturer you may want to change perfections because the puzzle is in your head and the solution is in your heart. There are three real messes for every imagined one, you lack the creativity to produce or enjoy real leisure. Imagine if you could throw all your resources into having a broken heart? There is a crossover point at which the armor becomes so restrictive that its protection isn't worth it. An armored heart doesn't beat as well. An open one does. You need

---

[3] If you are beside yourself it really is only a diversion. If you are inside yourself then you can be hurt enough to finally play with others. The only way to get you out is to smoke you out: tear gas. You won't come out on your own. We will have to send someone perfect in to get you, someone worth coming out for and that is a personal criteria that you better find out before it is too late. It is no accident who is sent. If you can still recover from love then it isn't deep enough love. Recovery is how quickly you can be "business as usual" when rationality claims special conditions should still prevail. Indulgence is claiming special conditions just because they can be justified. Psychotic is claiming extended non-negotiable special conditions. Life as an accident is the least satisfying unspiritual ground that can be fought forever for without ever being gained or lost. When something can be gained or lost it has an obvious end which is grounds enough for you to change the subject, but when it can be neither, then an end has to be a matter of creation. If this were an upside event it would be perfection but since you are being tickled by "this isn't it" the whole time it makes life on Earth Hell as preparation for the endless fever in your future.

to get in romantic shape by breaking your heart more often. The heart has only working parts but no gears. If even one little part doesn't work or if you seek to get even, you're dead.[4]

Broken hearts come unexpectedly if they aren't going to be reproducible. Love is the willingness to remain unprepared and take on the risk of never letting go, certain of losing, but winning each moment. Ironic is what love turns into in the mind, a kind of alchemy of unrequited romance.

But don't settle into the pain too much. If so, then there will be loss without found. It should hurt just the right amount. It should hurt until the dentist has scraped out all the pleasure, leaving nothing. A process which is seldom experienced without the curtain of pain relieving diversions.

It hurts, but what option is there? Where is Christiaan Barnard[5] when we need him and was he a happy man? I doubt it. Swapping out used parts like that. The ultimate cheat. I don't want a new heart, this broken one teaches just fine. It will even heal on its inevitable path to opening again. This is most of what we are here for. This is part of why we gathered together this meeting of hearts and minds called humanity in this location at this place. It is not so that the hearts could sit in the back with the minds occupying the voting seats. Only reason isn't worth living. The only reason that the heart seems so slow is the mind's dependence on it. If the mind didn't have so much to learn the heart wouldn't have to work so hard. It could break

---

[4] If you step into my beautiful office and I am down and out on the floor, maybe dead, what is the first thing you do? You make certain that my work has been saved. That is if you love me. If you are compulsive you make certain it is saved and backed up. If you are selfish you read what I have been writing. This is really the last writes. If you don't care about me at all you find out if I am dead or try and help me.

[5] To find out everything you wanted and more about the first heart transplant you don't go to science you go to literature. Specifically, *The Heart of a Dog* by Mikhail Bulgakov.

more, re pairing more, serial monogamy, often and thus learning about itself through more people. Until you can see everything in everything else you are on, notice that your only purpose is to break your heart.[6]

In the absence of a broken heart the mind takes over, in the absence of a broken mind, culture takes over. "You don't know how important I am," the mind screams without deference or reference to "you." "You" is, not are, the heart which, when missing a scheduled break, starves the mind of forced learning. The mind in relationship can only be related to another mind. Heart to heart, ashes to ashes. Would you like your shell broken? Some things are just more useful if broken. The tender perception available from the pinnacle of a broken heart is worth All: this.

There are so many tiny disappointments growing in the mind but never reaching the heart. So many little no's and knows. It is only watching the depth of a tear, the fall into you that allows the discovery that there is more to life than just worrying. There is no way out, the heart feels that and knows nothing; the mind keeps, like a retarded child, creating blueprints to nowhere, for everybody to follow away from each other. Digging your way into prison makes sense here.

"Hopeless romantic" is a mixed metafive. Mixed because hopeless is a function of the mind and romantic is a function of the heart. Until you can listen to Rachmaninoff without gagging you really aren't ready for the Hallmark store or another birthday.

I will have the night until it is over, then after a bit of the

---

[6] There are certain things I can't tell you, uncertain ones I can. If I tell you the certain things you will translate them into uncertain things anyway because you have your own certain keys guaranteeing you will be locked up. When you translate I blame you, I apologize. Sometimes I think I should have "I'm sorry" tattooed on my forehead but then realize that should I reflect on anything I would even get *that* backwards.

"blue hour," in between, I will welcome the sun again. Maybe it is time to give back to the sun. Maybe the sun's heart is broken too. Maybe light is its blood and maybe it needs company other than its own reflection: the moon.

Eureka! The solution to a broken heart is a new day for it to occupy. Lost in a dream will produce another cerebral outvironmental head-on collision. Enhanced in the dream will enhance it in the waking. The mind cannot wake up if it has to run from a broken heart. The heart is just doing its duty; it is following orders from another heart. The deeper the heart the more often the break. This is the connection that must be revealed more often. The connection between thoughts, beyond words all the way back to the stupidity we use to define ourselves.

All the differences in the world can't save you here. You don't need saving. You are here to flounder, a flat fish out of water. You are here to break, you are here to pick up the pieces of you, the pieces of another and to build "one" out of these pieces.[1]

The surface tensions, and all distinctions, are from how long, how much quantity you have into it and how that quantity makes abandonment unthinkable. You can't start over because you have already committed. You can only uncommit if forced to. The general power of a human being is in making a promise and revoking a promise, independent of outside circumstances.

I can't help thinking in volumes. *Volume 1:* You are too deep and too wonderful to be someone's cure for loneliness. You are not lonely and don't really trust the taste of someone who is. *Volume 2:* Your anonymity guarantees your lack of

---

[1] Never let your optimism show too soon. To do so preempts others' ability to brightly look on the side sticking them in a main course mind-set and setting them up for an owl baby meal, leftovers again.

responsibility.[8] *Volume 3:* You wish people would always keep their threats. Welcome to the big league of love. *Volume 4:* Your wrath will not be unleashed, not that it isn't tempting, but because if it were all the turtles in all the world couldn't put Humpty together again.

In other words: I bought a BMW for about five thousand dollars. It was pretty and red. I put about seven thousand dollars into it. I sold it for nineteen hundred. Do the math. It was as good an investment as any tangible thing can be. Each time I spent money on it I suspected there would be nothing else that could go wrong.[9] A new car would have cost less than maintaining this one. Finally I learned. I sold the car and bought a new one. Pay the price up front, the whole price and nothing but the price. Pay as you go takes a toll you won't wear well.

If somebody does something he is likely to do it again: pacing the cage. Some do it with sadness, some do it with rage, but pacing the cage is still pacing the cage. If somebody is guilty about having done something the likelihood of him doing it again is the only thing that rises.

Psychology doesn't tell us when to quit, math does. It isn't personal and if it becomes personal there will be trouble.

Time release amnesia, convenient amnesia. You can kiss someone once but can you do it again for the first time? Everything is now for the heart. Can you really live like that? Is anything less really living?

Temporary insanity is so common that it has become an offense not a defense.

This is the only way the mind can rise above the body. It must leave the body to do what it does well. The body does so much well but if we are to move along the evolutionary ruler to

---

[8] Anonymity doesn't even live up to its lack of reputation.

[9] An argument for mass trans sit.

ever-greater ability to seduce then a path will have to be burned between useful distinctions and behaviors.[10] So, it is leapfrog from the imagined head to the real body and then to the real head.

The loss of distinctions reduces to the lowest element of species. Reducing species to one and producing a lot of Jack and Jill asses. It flattens the playing field just as making useless distinctions makes the playing field needlessly bumpy. The loss of distinctions brings stupidity in the place of disorientation, automaticity in the place of creation and response in the place of stimulus.

If they treat your heart with respect they demean you, because respect is a function of the head. If they touch your heart with their heart they bypass the head, a heart bypass. If there is even one distinction you don't want to make about yourself you will not be a bootable disk, able to make hundreds of distinctions about your context, loved one or pet. The precision ever-present here is not really appreciated or goes without noticing. If all you learned from looking is the precision and never even saw anything else salvation would be yours.

You have to settle the, "are they worth it?" question right up front. If it comes up later it is too late and you will have already made a fool of yourself in front of someone who can't appreciate it. When you flush the toilet you had better be pretty sure your wedding ring isn't in there. Karma is the only aphrodisiac you need if you can stay present for long enough. The greater the sample rate and longer the attention span the more learning is possible.

---

[10] The mind currently thinks it leads the way but doesn't. We must have our hearts broken often enough that the mind can't hold to anything. Then the mind can create the future independent of but knowing the past. Voilá.

When I was little I found a diary of a Zombie. Their priorities are very different than ours. They always want safety and never want what they really think they want. They seek what they don't have in an attempt to get what they don't want and then think, think, and think, always missing the point. They are the living dead and part of that is wanting to be living. If they are washing the car they want to be making love; if they are making love they want to be washing the car. They are some wacko kind of un-folks. Zombies never know that there are repercussions to their actions and inactions. They don't know there are repercussions to their thoughts and what they don't think. They can see the world through eyes devoid of connection and love is the farthest thing from their minds' I. Sincerity tips you off to their unrequited lying nature. They never sleep, they just lie their way down and out. When I was a kid Zombies seemed pretty odd to me. I couldn't figure out what motivated them or how they got to be the way they were or why they thought I needed a babysitter even when I could make my own dinner. It seems Zombies don't really trust and they have a great facility for finding what they don't trust now which justifies what they don't trust next as they chain together a life of grim distrust.

The one thing that Zombies are afraid of, and I got this from reading between the lines, is holographic homeopathy. Given the newness of this field (I just created it) the Zombies are still flourishing in numbers but not voting enough to remain in control.[11]

---

[11] Zombies almost always have pets. Zombies are almost always dieting tomorrow, exercising tomorrow and going back to school or mother tomorrow. Zombies always have brighter tomorrows than todays, but they never come, the tomorrows either. Some Zombies consider a brighter tomorrow a cloudy day.

Spiritual Seduction

An evening of disrespect in a day of despair seems like love to a starved individual looking for warmth. It just doesn't generate enough heat or passion to keep on noticing.[12]

Once you don't have the option not to avoid consequences all consequences are optional and it is a matter of character which ones get taken. Taking all of them, if not compulsion, is the doorway to spirituality. Taking all consequences, everyone's consequences puts one in the power position of doling out consequences. If you try and avoid any consequences you are stuck in response, a loop. In other words: It is you who broke your heart.

Picking your nose is deeper than trying the anti-Karmic task of picking consequences. Empty, heartless play is a shallow, hollow and maybe deliberate attempt to avoid the upside or forced downside is a commitment to immaturity. The upside is always forced, there is no option. To fake it is too thin. The downside is not always forced. It is too easy to convince oneself it is real to need forcing. When it is forced it is exquisite; when it is contrived it is a masturbatory con job done defensively to keep life at bay and to play superficial. Too bad, as opposed to just bad enough or downright "bad."

It's all elementary if you are missing an electron: a chemical imbalance if you are not. Use mortality sparingly as a catalyst

---

[12] Loss of distinctions is the loss of attention—the death of consciousness. The only thing that wakes consciousness up is distinctions. When distinctions are lost part of consciousness dies. A big part of this is distinguishing between bits of consciousness. When consciousness is a whole, perceived as, it can be lost. When the bits are perceived, consciousness has a two-tiered existence, content and process, making it a little less tenuous and prone to the oblivion of negotiation.

Will you let go of a distinction when it seems to make you right? Will you learn if you need to let go to do so, or will you continue to hold guaranteeing that the future will be shades of the illusion of now? Life isn't worthwhile if all you have to look forward to in the future is shadows of illusion.

because you may get used up in the process. The future is yours: if you see. The future is not yours: if you don't see. Learning is as close to anti-Karmical as you can get, until you get more deeply into life, and life gets more deeply into you. Then you will know the Karmedic nature of Karma. Life will be less Calmedic and more Karmedic.

You can't play in the big leagues without big league consequences, the point of these is learning.

When your amoeba can break your heart you are ready for a real pet. When the real pet can break your heart you are ready for a person. When a person can break your heart you are ready for God. The amoeba gives little attention, God gives little attention, this whole thing must be circular.

If you delay compulsion for long enough you get love. People are compelled to compulsion, that is the nature of mind without a life to live.

The offence of adultery is blurring the distinction between the two people. The offense of monogamy is rubbing someone's nose in something repeatedly. The offense of bigamy is its honesty and shortage. On one level you can't be careful enough. On the contingent one you can't be risky enough.

A spiritual path is only possible once you can have instant intimacy anywhere with anyone.

If you know you will only get credit for completed homework and you know you won't complete it, why do you do any? Learning!

If you move away from the path of an open heart you are doomed. If you move into it you are ready for relationship.

There, that is what was in my appendix.

Appendix 4

A Brief History of "No"

A very young child can't say no. This is not surprising because she can't say anything. They have no's hurled at them from all directions. They are battered by no, beaten by no; traumatized with the imbalance of power but unable to express how unfair this whole deal is. Many people are inspired to say no for the rest of their lives out of the early no excesses they suffered. Parents are afraid of their kids, all parents. The tool they use to abuse, the tool that arises from choice is no. No implies a choice, but if so why does yes get said so seldom and when it does why does it not strike nearly as definitively as no? Why does yes usually mean maybe or under certain conditions and no, being much more something or other, spreads far and wide like a virus inspired to infect quality of life?

If the parent is upset when asked something the answer is always no. What is the likelihood that a parent will be upset? I am not a betting man but that is a sure thing. Will they admit their upset? No. Will they say no without thinking first? Yes. If they think first will they still say no? Maybe. There is an automated no which your past has learned to say to both present and future. While this conserves thought it also conserves upside.

Sometime around the age of two the child learns to say no for the first time and mean it. This is something the parent doesn't like. It is the first time you are called in the game of poker when nobody had really explained the value of the cards or what is in the pot. Your child says no, you panic. Parenting is never easy again. It used to take one, now it is a committee. Up to this point you had the luxury of pretending that you and your child were separate but your child didn't really exist. Now he does. He is in the way. You are offended as your child practices no. You even have to tell her what you are doing before you do it, setting up her no. You used to throw her in the car seat. Now she says, "I don't want to go." or, "Where are we going?" or, "No." You, insecure as you are, say, "Don't you want to go to the store with mommy?" "No." Ouch, too late for abortion. Life seldom gets easier when it gets more interesting. "Don't you want your diaper changed?" "No."

No has been so programmed into people that they will forego what they want just because a no may be lurking near it. As you grow up, without maturing much, no guides your life. Anyone in control of you exercises that control by using the word no. Though people's yeses often atrophy they exercise their no's quite regularly. They take them out on dates, to dances, to phone conversations, almost everywhere. I think no's should strike back—they are overworked and underpaid.

Stop overworking no's. No more no.

Think back: You remember the no's of your life. Oddly they seem to be more pivotal than the yeses. A no seems to mean forever while a yes seems to be a temporary condition. A no seems to be a personal attack while a yes seems to approve something outside of yourself, temporarily. Death even seems more closely aligned with no than yes. It would only seem to make sense that yes would be more associated with life, but it isn't. Yes is more associated with being awake and really living but it is nearly absent in the sleepy somnambulistic blah most people call life.

You thought you were in control when you said no. You said no to a teacher, "Will you erase the blackboard for me?" "No." And got to explore the decor of the principal's office. You said no to your parents and immediately a 50-ton weight came down from the ceiling. Your first love said no to you, or, and this gets very interesting, you were forced by fear, to say no to your first love, and you laid a little more brick on the graveness of asking.

Confrontation, rejection, authority, learning, abuse, and less all got associated with the word no. You avoided anything that looked like a no and given how insecure people are, you saw plenty of them even when there weren't any. Worse yet, if you ever said yes it caught people by surprise, and if whatever it was didn't turn out it became another argument for no. Yes is a laser gun while no is a shotgun. Yes focuses in with ever greater accuracy while no spreads out killing any possibility in its path.[1]

By the time you were in your forties you discovered that there was too much to do, too much challenge, too much of just about everything and in the face of all this abundance, that you really didn't even notice anymore, no was your first, last and every defense. No is de fence you build around anything that you don't want to share, see or enjoy.

No became the easiest route interrupting the formerly apparent connection between two points. No glued things together or apart and natural connections disappeared. Soon you could shake your head no and not even have to say it. Then you found another shortcut: you can just get a look on your face halfway between having just bitten into a lemon and discovering that you are about ready to throw up, a look so economical that anyone who sees it knows enough not to ask. You have found the perfect no. It takes no effort, avoids confrontation and you don't have to worry about ever getting close to anyone, yourself or anything else.

---

[1] Are these real differences between yes and no or just culturally defensive ones? Yes.

No is very powerful, uninspiring and, seemingly, risk-resistant.[2]

When Emily was a baby we said no to no, which, sort of means a yes. We didn't say no to Emily for the first four years of her life. Oddly, and let this be a yesson to you, in that four years she never did anything that we had to say no to. She seemed to be able to do a very uncommon thing and run around a very common assumption, she seemed not to be, listen carefully, basically bad but instead, BASICALLY GOOD. If we didn't intervene she always picked perfectly, and this was contagious. We got better just being out of control in her presence. What a wonderment what a tribute to yes, what a what a.

Yes, Yiss, yes yes yes, say oui oui oui all the way home, back to who you really are.

Inclusion is yes, love is inclusion, love is yes. Say yes, scream yes, whisper yes, say yes while lying. Si more and you will live in a much bigger and more fun world.

Personal history begins with what you have done and then offers up what you will do. At least this is educational, often it is motivational, moving one to do more or less of the same. So, think of the last year, how many times have you said no and how many times have you said yes? What is the balance of yeses and no's? No is defined as anytime you negotiated, had conditions or reserves. Yes is defined as anytime you affirmed without options. Any degree of no is a no while only complete yes is considered to be a yes. While this may seem biased it isn't, it is just the way things are. People hide behind no, they seek out no

---

[2] No doesn't really perform the magical feats it seems to. It does seem to though and in a world of fear, hurt and trauma seeming is the safest place to live, thus seeming becomes real. No just terminates and stays resident. Nothing outside you cares about your no's. Thus, what seems like a safe interface saves you no face at all. Your no face is no place with nothing to show for it. Say yes to no.

to protect themselves. If there are two hundred parts yes and three parts no the be-holder will be found behind one of the no's feigning invisibility.[3]

Imagine that you are going to be relieved of choice in the near future. You are going to receive a set of industrial sized balls in the male. These balls will each have one word on them. There will be balls with yes on them and balls with no. For each time you have said yes in the past year you will get a ball with yes written on it; for each time you have said no you will get a ball with no written on it. All of these balls will be kept in a big Stetson. Anytime you are faced with a decision you will reach into the hat and pull out a ball, that will make up your mind.

Do you want to play? If you were playing such a game what would be your exact likelihood, statistical, of pulling out a no? Of pulling out a yes? How is it to pull your answer out of a hat? How is it to have your current and future answers based on the past?

There is an easier way than the whole ball game. You could just say yes, an immediate resounding, complete and omnipotent yes, always. Don't worry, the details will work themselves out afterward. Don't worry you won't have anything to remember because no member will ever have been excluded. Just the act of starting with yes will inspire your context sufficiently that you will rise naturally. Play the YES game and you will soon surprise yourself more often than not could.

You may ask, and I will pretend that you asked, "Why do people say no so often?"

They say no so often for very many reasons.[4] One is that they want control more than anything else and one thing that

---

[3] The ratio is seldom like this but more often about 84 no's per yes. There is a tide with yes and a tide with no, the swings are uncontrollable as statistically one no leads to another. You cease to no-tice anymore and just no.

[4] The basis of reason is no. If you say yes you don't have to reason first. Yes plus reasoning equals no.

seems to give them control is closing things, which means saying no. If they own a store and they close the store then only burglars can get in. If they open the store, say yes to it, possibilities abound. When you say yes you open yourself to nearly unlimited possibilities, and you close yourself to control because you have to be ready for whatever happens next. Another reason for the preponderance of no is that people wish to know where they stand, they need to know where they stand and they can't stand not knowing where they stand. Know equals no. Your body doesn't understand silent letters, thus when you are seeking to know something it has the same response as when you are seeking to no something. Know-no. Lose the silent "k" and the silent "w" and you discover that every attempt you make at knowing has you noing. Knowing is limiting, knowing is terminal. You protect yourself by knowing, at least it seems so.

Another reason there are so many no's is that it seems to terminate further conversations, it seems to build a wall, a moat and an electrical fence defending what one perceives oneself to be from the future.[5] It is a kind of insurance against both downside and possible uncontrollable upside. It seems to kill two possible birds with one impossible known.

You often hide behind no, though your hiding is a bit like a very young child thinking he or she can't be seen because of closed eyes. If you are walking through a suspected mine field and you have low self-esteem, studies have indicated that you are better off closing your eyes than keeping them open. This is one of the mathematical arguments for blind dates.

No wears many hats. One of the standard ones is sarcasm. Sarcasm is saying no without admitting that you are saying no. You say something that you don't mean while having someone else mistakenly think that you do mean it. If you get caught you

---

[5] Don't run the electrical fence too close to the moat, especially if you ever let your kids or pets outside your sphere or no.

laugh it off; if you don't you laugh at whomever heard it wrong. Sarcasm is saying no without having the guts to say no and without admitting the responsibility that hides in no. When you discover the responsibility within no you will be inspired to say yes much more often. No is always an unsuccessful attempt to avoid the inevitable responsibility. Responsibility is the legit-imate air that a quality of life breathes.

Quality of life is based on the balance of yeses and no's, with seduction being the primary tool to tip the scales to yes and increase quality of life. It is political not to say yes or no but when you don't say either life hasn't really begun. Politeness is a thin, very superficial story about not saying no, thus keeping no hidden while treasuring its ability to keep nearly everything at bay. "I don't want to hurt his feelings; you can't just say no." The essence of politeness is sticking them in maybe when you are stuck in no, because somehow they can't stand the no but you can.

Your place in a company is based on how many people you can say no to. Slaves can say no to nobody, without dire consequences. A secretary can say no to a very few people. The big boss can say no to everyone else in the company. No defines the structure of companies and relationships. No creates structure.

Dignity is a function of being able to say yes or no freely, which almost nobody can. When you can say either yes or no you are at a magical place where you can perceive possibility. The moment you lean toward yes or no you leave the magic behind and wonder why things aren't as fun as they could be. Being able to say yes or no is to be, truly, in the driver's seat. It is a mighty place to be and you are a creature who deserves mightily.

It isn't the end of things when you learn to always say yes, though it is an undamned good beginning. Once you can say yes, you can learn to say a big yes. Big yeses are much more economical than little yeses. Little yeses are specific while big yeses cover broad ranges of love and inclusion.[6]

Playing big produces playing bigger. Playing small produces playing smaller, there is no hovering in your field of vision, crimping your future, ensuring your past. You already knew this at some level but your thoughts about it are saying no to how your behaviors are trying to teach you this particular lesson.

Along with the big yes comes the delightfully humorous big no. The big no comes in when something really is too good to be true. "Would you like a lifetime supply of gasoline?" "NO." "You have won the lottery, you will receive a million dollars a month for life." "NO." The more tempting thing you can say no to, the more you will discover that there really is a benefit in no. To use no defensively is to use it automatedly before you find out fully what you are saying no to.[7] No can be very useful but there are few places it will have you thrive. Most people set up their lives so that no is the most rational response. Altering the ratio of yes to no in your life toward yes will alter the context of your life having everything in your exterior design designed to contribute to the suitability and livability of your interior design.

The history of no doesn't have to be the future of no. No has a fairly dark future while yes has a light future. A balance between the two is essential but since the balance is thrown so much toward no wouldn't it be nice to say yes?

Yes.

---

[6] Love as most people use it isn't really love, it is an ulterior motive hiding in a short-term suspension of the admittance of your general tendency to run from things that threaten to influence you at all. Real love is inclusion, which is a very big yes in which head and heart conspire. Normally the yes of heart and the no of head balance out to a specific paralysis called life. Break out of this and the unpredictable becomes the norm.

[7] Anything done automatedly makes you less human, less of what you are.

APPENDIX 5

HAUNTED BY PERFECTION

You cannot get input fast enough from the outside, which is why there is no real time. We bring some of the smartest people here and within a day they reveal their blithering. In most people's lives diversions so prevail that a little self-knowledge is enough to inspire someone to jam a self-help book between your teeth for your own sake. Even the most gifted seldom get all the gifts due to a soul sale to that devil specialization which always results from a philosophy based in shortage. If you generalize your skills as a guitarist surely you have more strings attached but they sound as flat in the advanced stages of tennis as in the beginning, plus they are hell to tune.

Spirituality burns intelligence for kindling but it is enough to get the really big logs going. When you realize, deeply, that you can't enough (from the verb to enough)[1] no matter how much you get you won't stop whining the cheerlessness teams' lack of spirit about having so much to do and how "I am so busy." You will realize that nothing here is worth your time and yet all of it is worth doing and you will find some way to have others do it better than you ever would have because you just don't need to define yourself by your accomplishments, busyness, or grief anymore.

---

[1] I enough, you enough, he, she, it enough. This is one brick on the long road to selfless satisfaction.

There is nothing to do here and as soon as you are nothing you will know that. To nothing everything is possible. To less, varying degrees of choking block the air flow and you buy those degrees, bachelorsmastersdoctorsmegadoctors, you just waste your time trying to gain authority through credentials just to cover up that you can't sell. You can't sell because you have misidentified who the salesman is, who the client is and what the product is. Under these circumstances, this Great Wall of America, you have done quite well. Imagine if you could blot out the circumstances, or rouge them. Imagine if you could pull yourself out of the sticky content that threatens to end your life and then let it go on endlessly. Endlessly in the fodder department of endings right before the payoff.

What we are really talking about is raising yourself above the water level all by yourself rather than depending on something in your environs to do so. This is a kind of self-directed steam, rising ever rising. This can't be done within the confines of the physical world. The physical world is composed of actuals, which though more real than your thoughts, will only ever get you a quarter of the way home. If you trade in actuals you won't trade in possibles. If you have inter or inner course with someone other than me you either are biding your time, masochistic, or haven't yet learned to derive delicate sweet delight from the possible or potent. I will be the best lover in the world. I am currently the runner up to my future self. You too—I'm only talking about myself as a thinly veiled metaphor for you. If you didn't like my talking about myself that way you are not going to like admitting such things about yourself, not admitting is coming up with counter examples faster than you come up with evidence. Not bragging about yourself makes you a not sufficiently unabashed self-promoter to deserve in a timely manner.

When your deserving doesn't keep up your expectations take up the slack reaching the rocks first and are well and thoroughly dashed before you have time to reassess again. You will miss who you will be if you don't love completely who you are, then who I am, then who you are all the more.[2]

It is likely that if you spent your alleged lifesavings on one race at Kentucky Downs you wouldn't leave before you found out the winner. Whether what you have to bet is enough to alter the façade odds or the factual odds just has to do with how much you have cheated life. The more you have cheated it the more you look like the one who has fixed the race if you win, though the race officials claim it wasn't broken, and the stupider, but fairer you look if you lose.

But, let's talk about what is going on here. I am wandering along quite nicely when enlightenment hits. Ouch, I didn't ask for this. It didn't knock, it just kicked in the door which, of course, doesn't seem like a very enlightened thing to do. Two years one month and twenty-three days after the absolute pleasantness wore off I am sick to my stomach, sitting on the toilet all night each night trying to figure out if enlightenment is a gift or if it is not. It seems not to be but oddly I wouldn't want to be without it unless it leaves. It is like that, it doesn't ask anything but hints at everything. It constantly tests whether you want it or not. If you do it leaves or threatens to; if you don't it remains for one moment at a time.

I am a teacher, so I learn a lot. One of the things I learned first is that before enlightenment everything looks optional, after, everything looks mandatory. Under this everything, pre-perception of enlightenment is mandatory and everything post enlightenment is too. So either way you will be burned by light at the post-partum-pre-post death party and the best you can do is complain about it a little in unconvincing terms. Anyone

---

[2] This connotes the difference between a relatingrocketship and a relating-rockychip.

around you willing to listen isn't convincing enough to convince you that you are convincing them of anything but rather
keeping them from what they really should be doing but don't
want to do.[3]

You could try the doctor but,, he or she, if at all observant,
will let you know that you are not experiencing sickness but
excessive health. The kind of health that results from your pro-
cessing everything at such high speeds that nothing can get
stuck. The death of a procrastinator is seldom mourned on time
and death of what most people call life: later, afterlife. The one
choice they want to hold on to most tightly is the power to put
something, especially themselves, off. Lightly always demands
dealing with things in real terms quickly before there is any
chance to think. This super-health will be dealt with and it will
be speedy.

Imagine that you are playing cards with the boys, the girls or
the boys and girls. Then imagine that all night long you get the
best possible hands. You win every hand with the statistically
impossible deal. Everybody, including you, thinks that you are
cheating but can't figure out how and doesn't even consider
why. You consider folding but are too still in your morality to do
so. First they call in the law, Claude the local dull-witted
gumshoe, then the local priest gets conferred with, that's easy,
he is playing, and always losing at the next table.[4] Finally they
call in the best Las Vegas has to lose, well, a Las Vegas winner
is your loser. You can't get anything but perfect hands and you
can't help but win. You have one choice: Quit. The perception
that there are lots of choices produces lots of choices. The

---

[3] An artist in poster.

[4] Once I wrote on a dollar bill before I put it in the collection plate, I won it
back in a crooked game that evening. Another time I wrote something else
on a ten dollar bill and donated it to a political campaign only to receive it
back as change for a twenty from an inexpensive hooker that very evening.

moment you lost the ability to lose you also lost the ability (and willingness) to play. Isn't it grand to be dealt the hand and not know if you will win or lose? The only reason that you are still managing to get out of the grasp of perfection is that you are willing to disappear in the face of anything that works.

You are a clock without hands, a win without losing and this is enough to lose you what you thought were friends. Everybody in your world depends on a certain balance. Everybody. When this balance is upset, and enlightenment is the biggest upset to it there is and the most prevalent, you lose everything by winning all the time.

You sit down to write a poem and, yes, it is the best poem ever written. You didn't think I wrote this book did you? Yes, I didn't. It just flowed out of somewhere and through me on the way to somewhere else and guaranteed never to stop. Mozart had his wife read to him while he was composing, that way those ghosty parts of his mind so depended on by others could be amused as the real composing got done. As I write this I have had two hours of sleep in the last 30 hours, eight orgasms (my partner has had four times that number, all with me), my children are glowing, a beautiful blonde with freckles[5] who only says yes but only to me is coming in two weeks for four days; she will bring her thin beautiful legs and her flashing bright blue eyes. I am eating condensed milk as I write this and have just let go of a tightness in my lower calves that has half-plagued me since I ran a marathon without training twenty years ago and I have hundreds of people who love me deeply and as perfectly as they can and at least ten people who will do anything I say and that number is growing and I will never tell them what to do, and

---

[5] This blonde, the blonde, is not to be confused with a blonde earlier in the book. This one is mature and beautiful not frustrated, frustrating and beautiful. If you are even a bit upset at the characterization of blonde then you aren't her.

everything I look at, smell, taste or touch turns to a perfect complement for my existence, and my partner is jealous of the blonde which produces in me, her and the perfect blonde a kind of richness to every touch, thought and wonder in each of us uniting them into a pleasure spiral that can only be considered irresistible, unthinkable and neverending. As I write this I am so overwhelmed with love for you that I can barely write.

All of these are just the trappings though. They are easy to get trapped in and necessary to let go of. If you really want to win you can't care what you are winning, which is bound to have you collect things and people you can't stand. If you don't really care about winning you will have less of what you want and less of what you don't want; a kind of flat line life. Perfection is everything, the highest high getting higher and the lowest low getting lower. Perfection exists in each perception, in each fraction of a moment, if you have to do anything, alter anything, fool with anything that just isn't it and it is as far away from it as you can get.

This is a new high and in a matter of minutes becomes the new floor, the new low that I will never sink beneath. Yes, we went in the hot tub this morning. Yes, my nine-year-old son is kinesthetic and loves me like the plants do the sun. Yes, the trees speak to me as I walk out to get the mail.[6] Yes, my body supports my only move and constantly relates, converts and capitalizes on information I can't get anywhere else. Yes, yes, yes. I can't lose. No matter what happens I can't lose. It seems that somebody must wear this burden. It seems that, since I don't have any choice, it has to be me. I have it on perfect authority that this is the world that you live in too, but, very very oddly you don't notice it. It may not be a blonde for you, it may not be sex or writing but each moment perfection is handed to you in undeniable ways and you don't notice. You

---

[6] They tell me they are leaving just for me.

279

even turn up your nose and look, aggressively, for what doesn't work. This used to influence me. Jesus was on the cross and he was a bit bothered, under pressure, by the way some of the people looked at him and the way they didn't dress up for this special day. You don't bother me, love and bother are not on the same level and if you have them at the same time the best you can do with love is have an unrequited crush which does just that, crushes, thankfully, who you thought you were, jimmying with the lock on the door, as everything does, to your obvious perfection.

I want more though. Not because I want more but because I have discovered that more is always coming,, and that the one way to delay it just a little so I can have time to breathe or on a really special day, or on every day meditate, is to want it before it gets here. This wanting really does slow things down just one bit. Not enough to have light turn to sound, that is your game, but to have red light turn to green making everything a little eerie and slightly different than it was before. I am still able to avoid a full spectrum life some of the time and that is my current best definition of luxury.

What is your definition of luxury? I bet it is a slow one. I bet it has to do with ducks in a row or some condition being present that not only isn't present now but isn't present all the time.[7] I don't mean to be mean by pointing this out but that is the way you get yourself. You set yourself up and then are bothered if you stay set up or if you get knocked over. In a world of dichotomies if you prefer, even a little bit, one or the other you will always be at the effect of everything. Perfection is a cause and an effect without being able to distinguish between the two. Imperfection is that little moment when you finally see which

---

[7] You can watch the race calmly if you bet on a horse that can't finish but your security will be short-lived.

came first, the chicken or the egg, but then lose that knowledge and return to only being sure of things that aren't true.

Ya, I am perfect but don't make a big deal out of it. Yes, you are perfect and you ought to make a big deal out of that. There is really no imbalance here. Perfection, of the kind I speak, has no opposite because it is not in opposition to anything. It, like nothing in your life,[8] is beyond compare.[9] You aren't missing much by not seeing your perfection. You aren't missing anything either. You are perfect perceiving just what you do, but you don't know that which is perfect too. Earth isn't a very easy place to know perfection. I already let you know that your friends depend on your imperfections, so do the marketers, the market makers, the markets and everything in between. Imperfection is the only thing that keeps you going. The solution: to whatever: Of course, is to stop going, to run out of imperfection as a person whose pants are just too large runs out of them. You depend on problems, worries, troubles, tragedies and such to get you through your perfect day in a less than perfect way.

Say yes to perfection, your perfection and in that you will discover the perfection all around you. If you say yes to perfection before you say yes to everything else you will raise your confidence without budging your competence. This won't turn out well as it puts you smack dab in the inventory control of imperfection business. You have to practice saying yes to everything until you can really say yes to everything then you can say yes to perfection and then you have already said yes to God. At that point you can whisper your yes because it is already so obvious that it can't be missed, nor can anything else.

You are already perfect. YES.

---

[8] Get the humor of comparing here?

[9] Unlike other things this one is beyond compare.

Your basic, and deepest, problem is that you have nothing to lose. You keep trying not to lose things and if you only noticed that you have nothing to lose you could stop running inventory and get on with the life unusual, the perfect life. If everything started going perfectly for you it would take you about .231 seconds to spoil it. You need some preservatives since you never think anything fresh. You need some novelty, you need to want to slow things down and you need to want things that nobody else wants, you need to why things that everybody already knows, you need to what when there is nothing there, you need to when well before the fact.[10]

One of my secrets, I can't keep a secret. If you don't keep a secret you are a bad person but if you can't keep a secret you are a saint. Anything that is secret implies that you are being kept, to some degree in the dark. Lighten up. Say yes. Your body needs to learn to say yes. Your mind even gets to learn it. Watch the sunrise tomorrow and each day for the rest of your life; that is enough to start you out on the right and left feet. One of the keys to immortality is always seeing the sun rise and never making a habit out of it.

Perfection: yes.

---

[10] If you don't know the final score at half time you just aren't really paying attention.

APPENDIX 6

MEN AND WOMEN, BOYS AND GIRLS

When the woman turns into a man the man turns into a saint, and it isn't just a chest game anymore. I'm not talking about something you no about. I am talking about the way to get women to an earthly yes, from their current no, and men to a spiritual maybe, from their stuck earthly maybe. You will not know it when it happens, knowing is a brain cell function this is all cells in the body firing in unison, unilaterally, without dependence. The sign at the wedding chapel reads "Dependence Kills." It is a long way from being willing to being the attacker and a much longer way to being willing from where most people are. Do you see the edge receding or not see it at all?

Women have been oppressed for thousands of years. They need an allergy, or phobia to no to be released. Well, not exactly, they need to break the illusion of suffer age to free themselves. The only way they can break free is by learning to always say yes. I have said this sort of thing before in the book proper but I may not have expounded on it properly.

When you wake up in the morning the ratio of inside samples to outside samples should be about 100 to 1; this is the odds against your being influenced from outside. A great day is one in which your odds move from this 100-1 to 1-1 and then back again, otherwise you will be left with an imbalance, trying to get even, which always results in dissatisfaction. Most people are so uncurious and their existence so threatened they go 1-100 and thus justify holding their upsets.

When you find yourself nodding yes in an uncool exaggerated acceptance and, this is important, your jaw muscles are relaxed, not even tempted to speak or tighten, then you are outside the confines of your usual excuse for paradise.

When you wiggle a little new bit so subtle but non-negotiable that it forces your partner, with only noticing, to move fingers or whatever just so in an act of pre-orgasmic compliance and total acceptance, then you are matching mental and physical joining, such acts will never, can never, go unrewarded.

I can't spare you the truth, if I do I will strike out, just because you will react to it. You aren't going to like what I tell you next, but please, please, please, stick with it until you discover that I am not telling you anything like what you think I am telling you.

Women grow up to be men. Women have been oppressed for thousands of years by men. How in the world did the men do that, they must have had help? What price do the men pay for having done that? Women generate all the power on Earth and men harness it. Without women men would be nothing that they aren't now, fat, lazy and stupid, but without the men women would still be powerful. Women are much more powerful than men mostly because if work, or something, needed to be done, for the past several centuries women did it. If time needed to be waisted men did it. Diversions are men's work.

Men really do grow into saints as they lose their earthly trappings, until then they are worthless and after ascension they are perfectly though generally useful. Women grow into men; on the way there they stop doing stuff, stop taking responsibility for stuff and hopefully learn from the example of how men have done it "wrong" and don't get fat and lazy. Women run the game, men take the credit, women bitch about something because they can't really admit, until somewhat recently, that they are just tired of being oppressed, underpaid, overworked, misunderstood, pumped, beaten and forced in to motherhood and fatherhood.

Men have the luxury of doing philosophy, not that they have gotten very far with it in centuries.

Oppression is waking up first thing in the morning and having to have your attention off of yourself. Women live this every day, they also try and pass it on to men. Admit it women: One of your first thoughts in the morning is one of these, or something like them: "I wonder what he needs." "I have to get going." "I hope my hair looks alright and my breath smells good." "I will try and please (displease) him today." "I am just a rib gone nuts." "I can't put up with this anymore and I will have a breakdown as soon as I get the dishes done, the kid's lunches made, the kids off to school and the house cleaned."

Oppression begins small with attending to something outside yourself when you should be attending to something inside your self. Women are considered selfish if they attend to themselves; men are considered powerful. Men need to go back into themselves and discover their unexplored terrain, spirituality. To do this they will have to equalize their feminine energy with their masculine.

It happened just this morning, November 3rd, 2001. Karen entered my bedroom with a presence. She was a man, really a man. She wanted sex, she was going to have it and that was all that mattered. Sure, she loved me but she wanted sex not for me but for her. I'd wager dollars to fat free donuts that she had not thought of me or the dishes or the upcoming weekend once. She knew what she wanted and was certain to get it. If I had been the least bit insecure I would have lost it or at least not had a hard time with It.[1] This was new ground for her. She was only saying yes and she was, this is the most impossible position for a woman to have sex or no sex in, satisfied. She wasn't seeking anything she hadn't already found herself. This was, perhaps, the highest state function she had ever attended and way beyond anything she could have imagined. Noticing this and further noticing that she had no idea what was happening, I played. I will usually play given one millionth of a chance more or less. I acted like she had come in to cuddle and nothing more. I ignored the pheromones screaming out of her and threatening to drown the bedroom. She was the sexiest she had ever been, this is extreme, but I didn't react. I watched her do what a man would do in such a situation. I watched her sex drive fade, sneak away and resign itself from suspected intercourse to outercourse.[2]

It looked to her like she was losing something, moving from yes to maybe, moving from a fully furnished inside to a maintenance hungry outside, beside herself. Just because, hopefully, some of the best moments of your life were sexual doesn't mean you have scratched the surface of the best sex.

She settled down like a man does and began thinking, lightly, of other things, like the perfection of all things and how nice it was to touch me and be touched. She was new enough at this that she didn't get all the way to football. When it dropped as far as it was going to go I said, "Don't you think we ought to have sex?"

I am almost embarrassed, and she soon took off her pajama bottoms. We were playing bounce the chippy in typically profound, new terrain style, one orgasm, hers, to the wind when I had something to write. I picked up my book, always in reach and wrote this: "When you are having intercourse and you run out

---

[1] I believe that all references to a man's penis should be capitalized on. It is like a club with one member.

[2] Everything is either innercourse or outercourse and only one of these is on course.

of hands to touch your partner with, don't invite another person in, use attention. Focus on where you can't touch or reach. Attention is handy, especially in times like these."[3]

As I was writing I encouraged her to keep playing, which she did enough to interrupt my writing as I wrote: "You can't handle dis ease by just getting sick."

I put my book down, my thoughts down too and got down to it. Sorry no more de tales.

It wasn't until a bit later in the morning that I realized what had happened. We had an office meeting (I almost never attend these) what fun. Karen played the role of a man in the meeting. In short, doing her best, spouting off, not caring how stupid she looked and looking stupid a lot, coming up with great ideas but without the energy or interest in following through with them. Frankly, it turned me on. In all past meetings she had played the role of a woman and rolled over making me or someone else wrong for what had happened. There are two kinds of women in the world, those who complain about the oppression and those who don't. The latter are tolerated by other women, the others are only superficially liked by both men and women.

Women: Jesus Christ is not your personal savior. He encouraged your oppression. If you doubt this please read the bible and find out what message it gives women.

Women are encouraged to be careful, they are rewarded, slightly, for being subservient and punished for being aggressive or even neutral. Women are denied pleasure by having to fit someone else's timetable and only being allowed to punch the time clock, not the timekeeper (men). Maybe the tick of your pleasure doesn't match the tick tock of the clock or the treat you hope people derive from the work you put into holidays. And maybe if you are attending to the clock your pleasure gets

---

[3] The new millennium.

docked and you end up ticked off, looking around for something or somebody to blame.[4]

It is between the tick and the tock that your pleasure resides. The tick is a low decisive end point as is the tock. They end pin you to one illusion. You must call reality's bluff as you get more and more ticked off.

Women have to turn oppression into a positive. Men can't want to be free, they are already free and have done little with it.

Women are careful because it is the men who really call the shots. When you try and edit on the way in (which women do to be careful) you lose the benefits of brainstorming, mind-storming, and are an ass, behind an anachronistic peak, or peek, longing for length in all the wrong places. Left alone in his shade seeking the light. The light invites, the light reveals your asinineness as not being you, but you must look closely at what you don't want to see. Understanding is editing. You don't even get the whole message before you start trying to understand. You don't get the whole inhale before you start exhaling. You don't get a complete breadth of anything and become a narrow jumper with a big chest. Your cereal goes from tough to soggy so fast you miss the pleasant-perfect-present-in-between yous.

The seeds of the going down are in the rising up. The seeds of the rising up are in the going down. Let this lead to peace and perfect confidence in the harvest, that way you can stop doing all the time and start just growing into the pull of what you will be next anyway whether you *like it or not*. And the *like it or not* is the only part you can influence though do nothing with.

When you do, and women do a lot, men do a little and talk

---

[4] One of the initial steps toward women's liberation away from climax and peak oppression is easy orgasms. These are defined as deep, pure, two minutes or less with no electronic or stumbling male assists. Men are almost universally threatened by female orgasms but not obviously so. Sex begins for the man once the woman has had at least one big juicy orgasm.

or think a lot, you get in the way of perceiving. If you can, do, operate on half a chance you are quite unlikely to wait for more relevant data to reveal itself. Half-cocked may be length, it may be width, but it always excludes the more reluctant and most useful: depth. If you understand it in half of the first time, cor- rectly, there were not enough turns to reward attention. If you got it, understood it, in one occurrence it was not deep enough to reach any relevant part of you, for understanding always blocks further vertical progress. If it takes hearing several times you will whittle your illusion in a patternless way having think- ing advertantly seeking, like a light seeking missive, who you are.

Men bluff more often, if not better, than women do. Women don't understand as quickly as men because they are deeper. They understand other things. They spend too much time with their legs spread, thus resulting in philosophies that in one moment have them give birth and in the next have them try and have their hair look perfect. Thinking about how your hair looks during labor makes birth an expression of vanity. Labor is closer to free expression than most women get in any other context in life.

Oppression produces dissatisfaction but so much later that the overall oppression doesn't show it self. Women become con- vinced that if they win a battle they should keep fighting.[5]

As a woman you will be unsatisfied. As a man you will be

---

[5] There is something to be said for the old bee sting philosophy. It states, and I quote, "You never really find out about somebody until you see them stung well and truly hard by no less than three and no more than twenty bees at the same time." These bees should preferably be yellow jackets and these stings should be distributed between face, neck, belly and inner thigh. If they forget about you when this happens it is only a matter of time before they forget about you completely anyway. If you see it coming you can, maybe, do something about it. This is a little favor the bees do for us, I will get to the role the birds play soon.

oblivious. Neither of these are better but by progressing, by way of seduction to spirituality, both become short-term stops on the way to the best sex you have ever had and much more. You are a whore as long as you don't perceive and live from the connection of all things. But, thank goodness, names will break my bones but sticks and stones will never hurt me. And, a bird in the bush is worth two in the hand. So, you can get there from here, hear.

Young children are fascinated with watches and disinterested in time, that is enough to make one particularly, longingly, nostalgic. As a child it was important to me to have the watch on the correct time before I lost it. That way I would lose it at the right time.[6][7]

---

[6] I suggest that you listen to two songs on the subject of men and women and read no books about it until my book, *Men and Women, Boys and Girdles* gets released. If this topic interests you please listen to Dar Williams singing "When I was a Girl" and Uncle Bonsai doing "Men and Women."

[7] I'm glad I got this appendix out.

APPENDIX 7

DANGER

"I deliver things in code," said the universe, "otherwise fortune cookies would be much larger."[1]

You are lurking around the next coroner, looking for life, but in the time it takes you to die trying you move on just as you get through catching a fleeting glimpse of your own rearend disappearing. This would be fun if it weren't so consistent. If you could just think that yours were original sins. You can. That is what short attention span is for. It is so that you can live in a world of isolated non-events. It is so that you can miss the patterns and deal with one individual, case, at a time. Again and again and again.

You need to learn how not to pace yourself. Pacing is the rational, rationale, moral excrement left to let you know you are getting dangerously close to the present. It is a smelly hurdle which makes the border where your neck and shell meet. Anything rational, anything reasoned or anything ruled is something smack dab, a plug, in the way of finding out anything about who you really are.

It is your interface with time that defines in the absence of revelation. Almost everything is done when it shouldn't be, it is done sub-standard and though it is brought in on time it is

---

[1] "And more accurate."

brought in by time which is just not the hands, one short and one longer, that can carry the weight of anything worth doing. "Anything worth doing is worth doing forever," the universe says. You translate, "I gotta get this done as soon as possible." "This is perfect and complete fun," says the universe. You translate, "I can hardly wait to get done with this and get on with something really worth doing." "I will take everything," says the universe. You distort, "I do." "I am the one and only begotten Son of God," says the universe. You mutate into, "I am the one and only son of a bitch."[2]

Too much is negotiable. You sell out and then wonder why you are stuck in and up. You defend by thinking that you are better while saying that you are not setting up a battle between North and South which can only be solved later. There is too much talk and too little rhyme. Too much of everything but results. There is too much plain talk and too little appreciation of the kind of code the universe has to offer. You must be able to trans verse and then you will understand the perfect poetry all around you. You will be able to look at the frog poised on his pad ready to jump but not yet knowing that he can jump, but the muscles storing the data for him, so that when the time comes he doesn't say, "How high?" but merely launches himself starward. He is telling you that you have to look at exactly what is around you before you leap but that you can't possibly look where you leap. You have to look around you all the time and know exactly where you are before you move. The roots of discontent are in moving from somewhere, you no not where, to somewhere you will never know where while telling yourself that you lived happily ever after.

---

[2] Meaning that you complain about your mother. Don't you? Not necessarily out loud but always reserving the right to pass original responsibility on and on and on. Making one two then two three and so on and on and on. You wonder why you are bored. That's why.

There is only one way out of this. Any way you get out. You won't exit here unsatisfied. So you hold on to dissatisfied as the road to immortality. Get a key, get a clue, it doesn't really matter what you wear for Easter as long as you find most of the candy-eggs.

You could be left hanging or right hanging as long as you are hanging it doesn't really matter. You could store the future in your muscles and the past in your bones but why is the present relegated to no place at all? It is more likely that you will find the present in your body and the present in the things around you and the past and future in your mind.

There is a particular speed-relationship between both the hardness and the size of what you put in a blender and what you get out, almost no matter how long you blend. The recipe does matter, then philosophy, but never in the reverse order. You find the blender full and then think you pick what you blend. If you put a whole coconut in you are likely to pull out a damaged whole coconut and a damaged blender. But some flaxseed is just the right size to damage neither and have the whole blending be a waste of time. There is a magical blend which has the nature and nurture of that which is blended become something else, thus have it not matter that nothing is created or destroyed in the process. Earth is a slow blender. It is time for more of these, for as Buckminster Fuller said, "You just shouldn't burn the parts of your spaceship to cook cosmic marshmallows because then you would have to enjoy them as if they were in limited supply and that would have there be sufficient burden on the varied tasty treats here too great for you to bare making everything that you do a little more meaningful than it is supposed to be." In other words: You take yourself seriously because you misidentify change as destruction and unless there are huge elements of loss in something you don't think that it is really worth your time, and if it isn't worth your time then you are wasting yours, and if you are wasting yours then it is impossible to think very highly of yourself: isn't it?

This isn't a race, this man kind thing. It is many races and many kinds. It won't be resolved in your lifetime and you keep putting things off until it is resolved. There will be a curtain-call but it will be "curtains." This is already as fun as it gets and you suggest to yourself that it just isn't enough fun yet. That would seem to decrease your odds of getting out of this alive or, and this is more important still, being in it alive, or alive on time. After all, you can't be monogamous with just part of someone, and since everyone seems to have schizophrenia rising, you have to be monogamous with all of them. You may as well just be monogamous with everyone which defeats the purpose which is the point.

Have you noticed that when you feed a baby you love you open your mouth as you bring the silver spoon of ugly yellow squash paste toward him or her? Have you ever realized that the baby thinks you want to eat it, to swallow it like just another fountain of youth vitamin pill? Have you yet realized that when you speak it is the universe mouthing your own personal Lost and Found and providing the keys you need for a puzzle you don't notice in a time that you haven't arrived but are already in? You knead to hurry up and become an anachronism so that you can generate the next generation and auction off your stuff to the highest disinterested bidder. I bid you not, no, I bid you yes. I deal you every other card, myself the even ones and then we play them as though they must be separate until the resolution of one winning and the other losing. The hands go together, the odd and the even, we are supposed to get out of this together as one. So much DNA, so little time. So much code to express, to test and so much loss to experience.[3]

---

[3] Living homeopathically is pathetic.

Since most people are monsters to themselves, they don't know and don't notice they're haunted by perfection and just think they are haunted by their thinking. Being haunted is a bit like always casting a first stone or a shadow and often confusing that stone or shadow with who you are. Shadows don't bite, they don't eat, they don't love, or make love. Shadows just shadow. They follow you semi-exactly in their dark way defining, if one is fast enough to discover where the source of light lies and where it doesn't. Shadows almost. They don't even die. When you block the light the shadow existence is almost born and constantly bourn out by you. If you shoot a moose in the wilds you have to cut it into pieces to get it out. People see a fraction of it and then decide that mooses are odd creatures, bloody parts of things rather than big-nosed beautiful vegetarians.[4]

You aren't invited to the good parties, you don't want the one who wants you. You instantly, which is pretty damned fast, take anything for granted. The pain seems to reel you into a world of it, and seems realer, more real, than anything else after just the right while. Just the wrong while doesn't result in pain at all.

There is less everywhere but it hurts good by opening you. You, as defense, ignore the small losses until a big one comes along that you can't ignore. Ignoring is all you have practiced. So, you try it, you ignore again and again, successively throwing fuel on the flames of your inability since each attempt at denial is successful, wasted attention, but each attempt at acceptance is not. When you deny you focus your attention without resolution, needing glasses but not having them, in a state of emergency, emerging see: birth. Yet another loss, inspired by you, attention flagging you down, down down to a not-so-screeching halt. Your loss is not so original, either. You have to deal with

---

[4] I presume you knew they weren't really vegetarians. They are meat-eaters just like cows are. They eat that "healthy" stuff and live on the bacteria (meat) that lives off the "healthy" stuff.

little ones, ones you can't yet see. You have to find little losses, the sixteenth-notes and thirty-seconds. You need to feel your heart and mind when you look at your empty plate though you have just eaten but can't remember what. You wash your hands accidentally while washing the plate and don't notice the part of you, the handiness which goes down the drain. You don't get a letter from a loved one and you crash but can't justify it so you don't notice. Every ex-hail hurts because you miss your next ride to ecstasy. If you walk away from anything done or undone, there is no difference; it is still loss and if it is done it is easier to justify but no easier to swallow. What if they made vitamins so big you couldn't swallow them or so hard that you couldn't digest them? Every alleged-win and alleged-loss on Earth is like that so you end up living metaphorically and wonder why the story just doesn't end right. A simile seems somehow like a place to hide because it is just a bit more homey than a metaphor. When you think of the past it hurts; when you think of the future it will hurt all of this to ignore the little as-of-yet unin-flamed bit of discomfort, not pain, of NOW. Now contains no pain, only theory of pain. And if you have it in your head you have it in a nutshell. When you are practiced with little losses, you are ready, smiling not happily or understanding but includ-ing before you know what didn't hit you and you are including. You open the door and welcome in anything waiting there or happening along. The longer the door remains open the more you will notice that both come in and pass you by, and the loss will have company and with enough company it just isn't loss anymore is it?

Earth is a big Lost and Found, but really a big lost, lost, lost, lost, lost, lost, lost, lost, found, and lost. You need to find your own beat, your own rhythm or you will be beaten rhymeless. But when you say yes to loss you can't lose. You just open having every loss expand you.

You can't get ready enough, there is no such thing, you just have to wake up. You have to find the present lurking and stop it from lurking. Sign in the birth canal: "No loitering." You need to wake up into existential ecstasy: it is the only available wake-up on Earth. If you try and look ecstasy in the eye and say, "That is mine," it will, at best, be a lottery for you here.

Time is on your side given that you will always lose everything, thus you will ultimately open everything. Remember being young at Christmas and loving the presents, wanting to open them and deriving great joy in any opening that went on and something like blatant excitement when it didn't? That is your birthright each moment.

Earth tithes to you and attention is your collection plate. Not memory because that is too volatile to keep accurate count. Your parents told you a lot, too little it seems, but they never told you it would be like this. Nobody did. Nobody whispered it to you on the wind through the pine needles, in the frog's voice and the cricket's legs, "Spread'em." They, the people, didn't know because they couldn't stand finding out that they struck out and never noticed.

Noticing is the first step. Noticing something so small that it doesn't define but enriches you by the very non-act of not getting missed. It didn't get lost, it got found, seen, heard, smelled, tasted and felt-up, making you exist. It argued through your unique perception for your existence and it will never ever be silenced again. It is existentially singing your praises so often you don't hear it. It is you.

If you are saying no to something now you are saying no to something much bigger than that later. When you hear the singing you can read the writing on the wall and you will say yes now because it is too much of a risk to say no: forever.

A dog pees on one tree, then another, marking its terrain. Observation marks yours. You have become Sherunlock Holmes and the hills are alive with the sound of you, and all the future holds is fertile, not yet obviously animated images of you. There will be no more sneaking or skulking. There will be more getting bye, thus no more loss.

Stretch outward, upward, past the confines of skin, turning without to within.

Don't pace yourself, evolution frowns on that: seriously. Don't use time and space to graph you, defining your access, axis, to anything. The width of the band defines the width of the parade which not so obviously defines the degree of celebration. Nothing is yours, it's you, all you.

You may as well travel, safely, around a decent-sized city having sex, safely, with anyone who has been in a car crash, and lived, in the previous 24 hours. That way you won't run the risk of having someone too close who isn't upset. That may be insurance but it really doesn't ever pay off. The past is like that and it ensures your future pace.

Sometimes you can't make it one more step and you're paying attention, and you don't take that step. Other times you need to push yourself within an inch of lunch. As light, you need a full-spectrum life. As Antero says, "Reality checks don't bounce." Paying attention earns you interest making you interesting, which is as close to magnetic as you can safely be in the presence of so much magnetic media. In other words: Surround yourself with outcredible people and you will be too outspired to worry about your own little world. You will discover that the "terrible twos" are the wonderful toos. You will never miss a party again because you are the one, and everything is evolving fast enough to catch attention on the fly without stopping and without passing go or collecting anything. You will move so quickly that your turns exceed your inventory[5] and your turning

---

[5] outventory.

radius, making your shelf-life approach zero which reveals balance rather than seeking it and making all your sins point blank rather than near misses. Nothing is onething everything has in common. This kind of common denominator is always a successive divide and concur making each siege, every siege perfectly successful. Perfection is successive successfuls times zero. You are the highest common denominator, making you the universal solvent.[6]

---

[6] I love you, Pax.

APPENDIX 8

WELCOME

An Invitation

Our Family

Jerry is a monk with a family. He juggles homeschooling Emily and Judson, leading workshops, writing books, being available to our community and growing.

Karen makes the family flow and the business work. She provides a magical energetic umbrella for a network of hundreds of people.

Judson, when not reading, writing and 'rithmetic, has some big boots to fill. They are rubber and come up to mid-thigh. Judson is all over the property doing what ten-year-olds do best: playing.

Emily has the wisdom of a sage, the hormones of a teen and the natural ease of someone who is growing up softly, without edges.

Books by Jerry Stocking

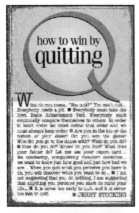

How much of your day is consumed by what you perceive you have to do? Rules you think you have to follow? Games you believe you have to play? What can you do to get out from under it all? QUIT! It's the one choice we never seriously consider. Quit something you feel you must do and you'll soon discover that you never had to do it in the first place. In the process you'll discover what you really want to do. By letting go, you'll experience the genuine fullness and vitality of truly living.

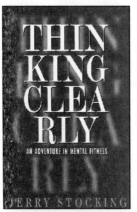

Your mind is capable of incredible feats and miracles. *Thinking Clearly–An Adventure in Mental Fitness* will help you experience it all. Most people are mentally flabby, easily angered and worried. A few people are mentally fit. They enjoy life and do more with less effort. A wealth of stories, illustrations and exercises in perception will bring to you a life so mentally fit that every challenge becomes an adventure and a delight. (formerly *Cognitive Harmony*)

You are enlightened. You knew it when you were a young child. You will know it again, soon. The question is 'When?' *Enlightenment is Losing Your Mind* is a philosophical exploration. It reveals a lot about who you think you really are. This book defines many terms, such as reality, spirituality, identity and the universe in practical and useful ways.

Laughing With God is a dialogue between two characters: a person much like you—with the same needs, dreams and desires—and God. Together they explore the human condition. The conversation emphasizes flexibility and the importance of amusement and playfulness over the seriousness which is currently robbing us of thoroughly wonderful lives. God is representative of the inspired bliss that exists in all of us. The person takes on the role of being truly ignorant, sometimes embarrassing, always sincere and continually willing to learn. (formerly *Introduction to Spiritual Harmony*)

There Are No Accidents is a novel which explores personal growth in fun and entertaining ways. Adventure, romance and spirituality wind through a story of love and living. The book is full of magic, things that we don't yet understand but will begin to appreciate as we open to the Voice of our spirituality.

Matthew Fox
"*Laughing With God* is witty, wise, humorous, and sometimes exasperatingly truthful—not unlike the Deity Herself. The author's dialogues with God sparkle with intelligence and humor. We feel encouraged to carry on our own."

"I have your books in my briefcase and on this 24-city tour I anticipate being the beneficiary of # Bill Moyers
your insights and experience. What a bold leap you have taken, one I much admire as a great example of 'following your bliss.'"

Dr. Bernie Siegel
"You don't have to agree with Stocking's God to be challenged and enlightened. Learn who you really are and about the true meaning of God and the place God takes in our lives. [*Laughing With God* is a] very interesting book."

Seminars by Jerry Stocking

⚭ A Choice Experience, Inc. ⚭

A tiny non-profit educational corporation dedicated to exploring human possibility.

A CHOICE EXPERIENCE, INC. IS DEDICATED to exploring consciousness, awareness, patterns and spirituality. Founded by Jerry Stocking in 1989, we have learned much over the years. We have discovered that there is much more to learn. If you are interested in exploring the fields within and finding both imaginary and real things to play with, then you may want to come and play with us.

WE THINK WE HAVE FOUND out what life is about. Life is about finding out everything you can about what it is to be human, then transcending the traumas of being human. It's about loving deeply, thinking very fast, being perpetually entertained from within and expanding both what we perceive as possible and what is possible for us. Life is also about growing, gently and lovingly, with others. For us, it is also about finding out just what makes us tick and how we can reveal the enlightenment within, glowing naturally in the wonder and mystery of life.

OUR COURSES ARE OPEN FIELDS in which to play. They are fast, fun and score a "10" for danceability. We invite you to come and play.

YOU DESERVE IT!

A mini-course in ecstacy. Learn to develop yourself naturally so that you get what you really deserve. Led by Karen Bates, a longtime student of Jerry Stocking. Karen has the empathy to understand you and the toughness to see through your unproductive routines.

ILLUSION CONCLUSION

The IC! Course will be challenging to your limitations and provide an environment for who you are to shine through illusion. Jerry Stocking leads you into a world where you can explore your life without illusion. When illusion disappears you can see clearly the world around you. The course consists of five class days and three integration days and takes place near the foothills of the Smoky Mountains in beautiful Northern Georgia.

COMPLETION OF THE IC! COURSE IS A PREREQUISITE FOR THE FOLLOWING:

Personal Renaissance

One-week residential course in which you will repeatedly bridge the gap between playing deeply within yourself and playing in the outside world. You will study *General Harassment Theory*, the process of causing a unique disturbance wherever you go. Rid yourself of fear. Operate a backhoe. Prepare for deep success.

Let Yourself Glow

Two weeks of peace in residence in beautiful Northern Georgia. You will be pampered but not indulged with meditation, massage, philosophy and peace. You will eat great food, talk deep philosophy, sit and dip. You will play indoors and outdoors delighting in what is possible for you. Watch out for enlightenment.

Parenting Course

The most important job on the planet can be the most fun, too. Good kids make for a great life. Let's explore how to grow up perfectly. Role playing, tips, tricks and practical application included. This is a four-day course in residence.

OPEN TRAINING

One-week open training course in residence for a maximum of four people. Tents and healthy food will be provided. The coaching and assignments will be as personal as they can get. You will have time with Jerry and other people around Clarkesville.

Illusion Conclusion

Come out and play!

LEAVE THE WORLD OF ILLUSION WHERE EVERYTHING, EVEN WHAT YOU CALL HAPPINESS, IS JUST A DEGREE OF SUFFERING. **You are invited to attend a very special course, Illusion Conclusion (IC!)**, where you will discover how incredible you are and always were. **The IC! Course** will be challenging to your limitations and provide an

environment for who you are to shine through illusion. **Illusion Conclusion** courses are held at the foothills of the Smoky Mountains in Northern Georgia, with five days of coursework and three integration days.

You are being held hostage by illusion and probably don't even know it. As a four or five-year-old you were full of energy, curiosity, spontaneity, movement and playfulness. Slowly illusion has replaced these qualities, choking your aliveness, making your body stiff and limiting your thinking to repetition and structure.

Illusion isn't nice and isn't necessary, but its nature makes it tough to find, even when it is all around you. If you put a frog in a pot and slowly heat the water, the frog will soon boil because it doesn't notice the slight increase in temperature. It will not jump out of the pot. Illusion slowly takes over your life, too slowly for you to notice. Light is the enemy of illusion because it reveals illusion as illusion. Light is fast; illusion is slow. Ridding yourself of illusion speeds up your thinking, making it difficult for illusion to catch and bind you. Is life, the world, going too fast for you? Are you too busy? The less encumbered you are by illusion the faster you will be, thus the slower the world will be relative to you.

Life gets easy—light—enlightened.

Call and register today.   **800.899.2464**

Come to the Course, or get the tapes, then come to the Course.

If you want to listen to IC! Course tapes before coming to an IC! Course, you can get the 24-hour Illusion Conclusion Course on tape, complete with a booklet including diagrams. The cost for the tapes is $149 and we reduce the tuition for your IC! Course by $100 if you have purchased them. We are a nonprofit corporation and use the proceeds from tape sets to fund consciousness research and expand human horizons.

We had a professional bowler call to return the tapes. "I listened to almost all of one side of one tape and I don't get it," he said. He agreed to listen more. He called back three months later having listened to the entire tape set three times. He was asking philosophical questions, had deepened his relationships and, his bowling scores had increased. He attributed his newfound delight to the tapes.

A CHOICE EXPERIENCE, INC. • PO BOX 2422
CLARKESVILLE, GA 30523 • 800.899.2464

People Playing

Yes

Yes

Yes

THE EDGE